EVERYWHERE IS SOMEWHERE

EVERYWHERE IS SOMEWHERE

Naseem Khan

Bluemoose

Copyright © the estate of Naseem Khan 2017

First published in 2017 by
Bluemoose Books Ltd
25 Sackville Street
Hebden Bridge
West Yorkshire
HX7 7DJ

www.bluemoosebooks.com

British Library Cataloguing-in-Publication data
A catalogue record for this book is available from the British Library

Softback ISBN 978-1-910422-39-7

Printed and bound in the UK by Short Run Press

*"While identity is a crucial place to start,
it is a terrible place to finish"*
– *Gary Younge, 'Who We Are"*

Contents

PROLOGUE

It's a long street, heading way down from Trafalgar Square – though not long enough for me. It is flanked with historic notables. I make my way under the gaze of one after another. Fixed on what? Empire, of course. Glory. Legacy, fame. An air of entitlement still surrounds them even now, decades after they've gone. Their lives – so easy, so pampered and protected. Barouche at the door, flunkies springing to attention in spotless livery: to the club, James, to the House, to running the country. And now?

I am not part of this grand tradition. An interloper. Born here but with no British blood. Half of my roots are deep in icy wolf-howling Schleswig; the other half in the baked heat of Central India. And right now I am on my way to one of the major portals of the great British tradition. I drag my feet. I allow myself to dawdle, to cast a scowl at Montgomery and an unnamed Nepalese soldier. In Parliament Square I pass even more worthies. Then I turn into one side street and another and come face to face with a sober red-brick building, the Arts Council of England.

It's got to be worth it, I tell myself resolutely, as the automatic doors swish apart before me. As I'm processed through HR, as I am given my plastic pass, as they say, "We'll get back to you with details of the staff pension scheme." I shudder.

I am giving up freedom on the range for this – freelancing, writing, working with an innovative consultancy on ways to transform public space. All that, for a staff pass and a pension.

It is Usha's doing, I think as the lift takes me up a floor. Always watch out for the good and the noble, and Usha – a friend who has gradually morphed into a grandee – is amongst the noblest.

"I want to talk to you," she'd said briskly when she'd phoned months before. "You may have seen I've been appointed to sit on the Council of the Arts Council..."

"Well, not exactly..." I hedge.

"And frankly, Naseem, the whole issue of cultural diversity in the organisation has stalled. There's nothing going on."

I can see that. It's years since I wrote 'The Arts Britain Ignores' that

1

started a major re-examination of what British culture meant now. And for a time there'd been initiatives and projects and aspirations. But leading to what?

"And I intend to give a boost, Get it back on the road. And this is why I am calling you. I want you to help me."

I start to say something but Usha carries on, "I don't have much time to talk now, but I have persuaded them to create an officer post. And I want you to apply for it."

She can't see my expression but if she could she'd see there is no way I could work for the Arts Council. I am a hunter-gatherer. I favour uncertainty and like not knowing what's around the corner.

"Think it over. You don't have to make up your mind now."

I say I will. But I already have.

"Have a look at the advertisement. It'll be in Monday's Guardian."

I look at it – 'Cultural Diversity Officer'. I do not apply.

Usha rings again. "We interviewed", she says, "But we couldn't appoint. We're going to re-advertise..."

"I really don't think so, Usha..."

There's a pause, and I can hear her drawing a breath. Then she says with slow emphasis, "Listen. I want to tell you something." Pause. I wait. "If you want to change things," she goes on, "There is only one effective way – and that is *through institutions*. It is the only way! Listen to me, I know what I am talking about."

There's something weighty and almost sibylline about her words and they stop me in my tracks. How can I not take her seriously if I want to change things? And I do, I still do want to change things, even after all this time.

The stories, the struggles, the unanswered questions about what it takes to actually belong to Britain – they're still all here. I don't have to summon them up.

Memories of my father's humiliation as he searched for the respect he craved. Resolute black theatre companies exposing racism in rickety halls. All the tenacity needed to unearth quantities of artists, writers, dancers, singers all from different parts of the world that went into 'The Art Britain Ignores', and to try and dig out channels so all that talent could flow into the mainstream.

And still so little happened, so little real progress towards the equal society we envisaged. Over and over again, the questions raised about identity and Britishness: 21st century anxieties of Britain that have grown and grown and at times turned toxic... Can we ever learn to live together?

2

PART ONE
INVISIBLE

CHAPTER ONE
1946

The house is so quiet it feels odd. When Abba's here, it's like the timetable at school except there are no bells. We all know exactly when it's time for him to come back from surgery, to have his morning coffee, to go out on his doctor's rounds...

But Abba's not here and is getting further away by the minute, and Amma is sitting at the table by the breakfast room window smoking a cigarette in the way she'd never have dared if he was here.

"Where is he now?" I ask.

"Not again!" she says when I get my school globe out from my satchel but she traces his journey for me again. Way, way round my rickety globe, over green or brown countries and spiky white-toothed mountains where snow never melts. And now he's landed at Rome and a letter has fluttered onto the hall mat. At last.

It's so thin. We both hold our breath as Amma carefully prises it open. "Onion paper," she remarks as she pulls the sheets out and they puff lightly like dandelions. "Be careful! It'll tear."

"He's half way," says Amma reading his letter. "They have to stay the night in Rome so the plane can fill up with petrol. Of course when he first came to England aeroplane flights weren't possible and it took him weeks and weeks to come by sea."

"And does it fly to India after Rome?"

"No, not even then. It's such a long way. They'll stop in Cairo and the airline have organised for the passengers to have a picnic at the Pyramids. You know about pyramids?"

Of course. "And mummies."

"And then after that on to Bombay."

"But he'll be back before my birthday, when I'm seven? He promised..."

But it is odd. While we're in Birmingham, with Amma's forsythia that she loves flowering outside, Abba is sitting under the baking sun eating sandwiches next to pyramids. And then he'll fly on to India where he's told me children like me fly kites from flat roofs and eat mangoes that are so juicy I'd have to sit in the bath to eat them. For a treat, he'll take me on a Sunday up to Five Ways to a large shop called "Ffulkes Furriers". We stand in front of its enormous windows for a long time. They are totally filled with a thick imitation jungle with lions and tigers prowling through it. We never get tired of it. And "That's what India's like," Abba finally says and takes my hand. Tigers and kites and mangoes.

At school a few days later, Miss says we are going to have a lesson about a very special man, in India. She starts to write on the blackboard spelling it out very slowly, "Ma-hat-ma." I wave my hand in the air. "Miss, Miss!"

"Quiet, children!" She continues to write, "Gand-hi-ji."

"India! That's where my Daddy's gone. He's in India!' I shout.

She stops and puts down her chalk.

"You must tell us all about it when he gets back." And she turns to the class, "How lucky Naseem is to have such interesting parents,' she says. "Isn't she?"

"Yes, and my Mummy's German!" I carry on proudly. But that doesn't seem to go down so well.

"Germany's rubbish," says Robert in the playground later. "We beat them hollow. My Dad says Germany's finished."

"Isn't!"

"Is!"

I try to kick him.

"*Kwatsch!*" says Amma loudly when I tell her. "Finished? Don't listen to them. They don't know what they're talking about." She snorts crossly.

How could Germany be finished? Parcels come from my grandparents Oma and Opa and Tante Else now the war is over, all decorated with fresh pine twigs and full of little sugary treats. And the German man who was a prisoner of war brought me my marvellous china doll whose eyes close when she goes to sleep. She's better than any dolls other girls have got. It really is *kwatsch*. I try out the word, time and again. '*Kwatsch*!" It feels rude, like spitting.

But it's a long time till Abba comes home. I've decided to learn all the bones in the body so it will be quicker for me to become a doctor too when I am grown up. And I've got a new Enid Blyton book about a magic faraway tree that I'll read in my private den that's the air-raid shelter under the stairs.

I get in everyone's way. "Your nose is never out of a book," says Mrs Smith who comes every day to clean and is always shooing me from one place to another. I complain to Bambi whose head with his great antlers hangs over the stairs: I stroke his dear rough fur. I hopefully tap the big old barometer in the hall, although it never says anything but 'Change', change never seems to come.

And then when I come home from school one day, the hall is full of suitcases and packages and big parcels stitched into white cloth. And my Abba.

"Ah, here she is! My little girl." he exclaims, holding out his arms.

He looks different – he's browner and his clothes are all creased and floppy as if they don't fit properly.

"You've lost weight," Amma says. He doesn't smell the same either. But his face has the same rough feel and his hugs too.

It's all such a mess. Presents are all over the place, covering the long red runner up to the breakfast room door, and Abba keeps opening packages and getting out more and more. Mrs Smith will not like the mess.

"Here," he says, holding out tiny little containers of salt and pepper. "This is what they gave us with our meals on the aeroplane," he chuckles. They look as if they are a tea service for dolls. "You can have them. Take them. You can play with them." And then he opens even more.

Usually I'm told not to chatter, but today he's the one who's chattering, and even laughing too. So we all do. It feels as if it's everybody's birthday. "And look at this..." He hands me a tiny book that slides into a metal case, no bigger than a postage stamp. Inside there's Indian writing on every page, but so tiny. Abba puts one page behind a circle of glass in the cover and the words immediately get bigger. "It's the Qu'ran," he says with reverence, "All of it, in miniature, every word!"

"Oh! Smell this," exclaims Amma, opening out a carved wooden box. Something lovely and warm creeps out, a secret perfume. "Sandalwood," she says softly. But now Abba's already passing her a smaller package that's wrapped up in newspaper – "Leave that! Open this!" – and tied with black thread instead of string. "Real gold," he points out proudly as she takes out six thin bangles. She eases them over her wrist and holds up her arm so they clink and glitter against her dark hair.

"And bangles for you too..." I can see mine are much, much nicer. They're made of glass and are red and silver and they shimmer like sunlight. "Glass!" says Amma with a 'tch' sound. And she takes them away for later. Next I get two dolls. They're both made of white cloth and stuffed so they feel hard. Their arms and legs are stiff and can't move; their eyes are buttons and their mouths are stitched on with black thread. It makes them look very mean.

7

"And this," he hands me another newspaper parcel, "Is specially for you from your Aunt Fatma."

Inside there's an Indian outfit – a pretty blue dress with flowers on it that I like. There's something else with it – plain and much brighter blue and very very shiny. "Those are the trousers that go with it." Trousers with a dress? Whoever does that?

Abba hands them to me.

"Why don't you put them on?"

They are enormous and feel slippery.

"But they're too big, Abba!"

"No, no." He's impatient. "Look, you pull this string that goes round the top, like this." He tugs at it hard and all the shiny material bunches up. I don't like this at all. I feel uncomfortable and stupid, all bundled up. The dress is nice. But I shall hide the trousers.

"Can I take them off now?"

But Amma is opening another bigger parcel so no-one answers. Out come skins of three dead animals.

"They're leopards," Abba says. "Feel how soft they are." They look like the animals in the window of Ffulkes Furriers. But with no animals inside.

"You can have them made into a fur coat."

Maybe he shot them.

"And there's a letter for you. It's from your cousin Iqbal. I know you'd be best friends. He's just your age. You'll need to write back to him."

After I've had supper and listened to 'Dick Barton' on the wireless, I'm sent upstairs with my presents.

"Can I have a story?"

"Nearly seven's too old for stories. But you can read. I'll bring your milk and potato crisps up."

I gather up the bangles before Amma can put them away, and the dolls with their dead eyes – and the horrible trousers.

"Just look at these," I say to Bambi, as I pass under his furry nose on my way upstairs, and I make sick noises.

And next morning all the packaging has gone. All the boxes and cases are tided away. All Amma's brass ornaments – the kettle, the warming pan – she loves, and that Mrs Smith polishes like a machine, gleam as silently as ever and the barometer still promises change.

Abba is already downstairs in the breakfast room looking through all the letters that have arrived and that have been waiting for him to come back. The clock on the sideboard has stopped and he's wound it up. I sit down at the other side of the table by the window.

"Gerda," he calls, "I'm ready," and Amma comes from the kitchen with his fried eggs and toast, the same he has every day. I can hear the Birmingham Post and The Manchester Guardian come through the front door.

"Shall I go and get them?"

"No, finish your breakfast."

Abba doesn't like talking at meals. I watch him cutting up his eggs. He does it very carefully so that the yolk runs evenly onto bits of buttered toast. At the end his plate is quite clean except for a few crumbs. He puts his knife and fork down in the exact centre of the plate. The little clock chimes.

"Hurry up," says Amma, as she comes in and clears our plates. "You've got to get to school. I'll get the car out."

While I find my coat and hat, Abba stands before the hallstand looking at himself in its mirror, making sure that he is tidy for his surgery. He's quiet and he looks at himself for a long time. He's gone back to being normal English, wearing his usual three-piece suit with the white handkerchief peeping out of the top jacket pocket. He's got his English smell again – not his Indian smell – from the bottle of Yardley Devon Violets.

Do people change when they go to different places, I wonder. Do they turn into someone else? Just now it's as if he's never been away.

"Can I come with you?" I love sitting in the surgery while he mixes medicines in his little dispensary room. The strange smells, the huge glass bottles, the tiny regular clink of his measuring glass.

"No, you've got school. Maybe after school, if you're good."

"Hurry up," scolds Amma, and I jump. "Where's your hat? Why can't you ever take care of your things?"

Abba is picking up his doctor's case from the cupboard under the stairs. There's a second case that sits beside it and looks just like it. It's his surgeon's bag, he says. But he never uses it.

I find my brown school hat – squashed again. "Do I have to wear it? The elastic hurts."

"And your satchel... And look at your gym slip," she scolds. 'The belt's all twisted, and..." she pulls my knee-length socks up that have slipped down.

'I'll see you after surgery," Abba says. "Have my coffee ready." The front door with its panes of coloured glass closes after him with a mild shudder.

The minute he's gone, Amma straightens up, and looks out of the hall window.

"Has he gone? Are you sure he can't see?"

She watches as Abba crosses the road and I know just why. Sure enough, the minute he's safely disappeared into the back door of the surgery opposite, she reaches for her handbag.

"We've still got a few minutes, there's no hurry," and she takes out her packet of Players.

I sit in the front seat as she finally backs her car out. I peer right and left, "No-one coming."

Looking back at our house – 11 Rowlands Road – it looks like a picture book house, square and solid with its crazy-paving drive leading up to the front door. There are just four big houses here like ours, and then they get smaller and smaller going down the road. But ours is special. For a start it's got a name, even though it's *kwatsch*. It says 'Elim House' on the doorpost, and then under it there's a brass plate that Mrs Smith polishes every day with 'elbow grease' that says 'Dr A.W. Khan' and then lines of Abba's degrees, and 'Residence Only' in case any of the patients think they can knock on the door wanting to be seen.

"Why's it called Elim House?" I call to Amma.

Amma shrugs. "That's what it was called when your father bought it."

"Can't we call it something else? It's boring."

The houses in school stories have lovely names like Pear Tree Cottage or Oak Tree House. "We could call it 'Cherry Tree House' – we've got a big cherry tree in the front garden. Wouldn't that be nicer?"

"All this traffic." says Amma testily. I know I'm going to be late for school again. It's all because of her cigarette. She's having to go slowly down Coventry Road with all the lorries and buses and we've only just passed Gilbertstone's row of shops. There's the post office where Amma gets the Sports Argus so she can check if she's won anything on the football pools (but she never does); and there's the hairdressers that's full of big rumbling hoods like something out of Dan Dare's space ship in the Eagle; and Pollards the electricians with the man who Amma says wears a wig.

Amma gets bolder, "Ach – enough of this," and she overtakes the big yellow double-decker in front. They hoot at her. We pass the Wagon and Horses at the end of the dual carriageway – and maybe there really were wagons and horses here once upon a time. When we turn off into the road that leads to Solihull, we're driving up roads that have more country-names – Mill Lane, Manor House Lane, Lode Lane – and then we cross over a very still canal with an overgrown grassy towpath and big old trees.

"I love this part," I say. She slows down.

"It reminds me a bit of Far Forest," she says. When she talks about Far Forest Amma gets a dreamy look. "You won't remember it, you were too young: the little cottage we lived in – just you and I – during the war. It didn't have electricity or running water, just a well. And every morning we used to walk over the fields to get fresh milk from Farmer Lingon's farm. I grew vegetables..." She sighs. It sounds lovely – nicer than Elim House. But how can I remember? I was just a baby.

The road gets more crowded as we move into Solihull. Amma throws her cigarette out of the window. "Of course I couldn't let people in the village know I was German in the war. I had to pretend I was French."

If we lived in Cherry Tree House, everything would be different. Nobody would argue. We'd always be happy. I'd have a pony and go to ballet classes and have best friends with names like Betsy and Bunty. And sisters.

I was right. I am late. The bell's already rung and I'll have to run to get there before they do the register. Amma pulls the car to a halt. "'Quick, don't forget your satchel." I look back and she is lighting another cigarette.

CHAPTER TWO
1948

Feet are the worst. Hands are very difficult to draw – inside is nothing like they are outside – but they're not nearly as bad as feet. I'm sitting upstairs and I draw leg bones very carefully, checking back in Abba's Gray's Anatomy to make sure I've got them right. The swoop of two long bones is nice to draw, all the way down from the knee, from the patella to, well... My feet look like bunches of little pebbles.

"Have a look in your Encyclopaedia," suggests Amma. "There's probably something there you can copy."

That's no good. I already did. Arthur Mee covers just about everything you could ever think of in all the ten volumes of his Children's Encyclopedia – how light is made, why volcanoes explode, stories of the great painters, tales of the Empire. Everything, apart from feet.

And then there's a picture I can't keep away from though I hate it. It's something that really happened in India, and I can see it even when I shut my eyes. English women with white sad faces stretching their hands out through a barred prison window. The heat – even the palm trees are wilting – is immense and they are desperate for water, which is why the next bit is so wicked. Outside are three Indian men in turbans and bare chests and one of them is mockingly pouring water from a big bag full of it right onto the ground in front of the women. And the men are all laughing. It's true. It really happened. It says so in my Encyclopaedia. But Arthur Mee also says, 'In India, British rule was of infinite advantage to the people. Their welfare was made always the first consideration.' So why were the men so cruel and ungrateful?

I rapidly turn the pages. I find out how to do magic tricks with a penny and how to make a pin-hole camera. But no feet or skeletons. A lot of the Encyclopaedia is boring – hardly any colour pictures at all – and then I stop at the story of Baldur whose mother dipped him in magic potion when he was small so that no weapon would ever be able to harm him. But no-one noticed that a small oak-leaf had got stuck underneath one of his feet until...

"Naseem! Come on down! Quickly. We need to go!"

... until wicked Loki...

"I don't want to have to come upstairs and get you!"

I sigh, close the book and slowly go down, bumping down step by step.

"Do I have to come?"

"Yes, of course you do. We're all going. Mrs Cheney likes to see you. And you like her house – don't you remember the summer garden party?" No, not really. "The time when the band played," Amma starts to redo my plaits, and it pulls and hurts.

"Ouch!"

"And you got up in front of everyone and danced and danced, don't you remember?"

"I think so." How can I remember so long ago? It was before I even started school.

When Abba turns the car into the private drive to Mrs Cheney's house, it's as if the whole world has gone to sleep. All the sound of traffic outside stops and we crunch along the long curved driveway under very old dripping trees. At the end, over an empty lawn, is the large sprawling house. And that looks asleep too. Its upstairs windows are all covered with blinds. Abba rings the doorbell and it rings deep in inside. For a long time no-one comes.

"Are you sure it's the right day?" he asks.

"It's Mary – she's getting on."

We are led by Mary in her black maid's dress through a tiled hallway with dark wood chairs. A life-size bronze figure of a little black boy sits on one of them. His cap is on crooked and he wears a cheeky grin. Someone has fixed a sprig of holly to his metal jacket even though Christmas is over now.

"Come along," Amma whispers as I linger.

Mrs Cheney is standing up waiting for us at the far end of her very long dark drawing room. Long velvet curtains almost shut out the view through the big windows down to the ground, but there's enough light to help us make our way between lots of little tables here and there with china ornaments on them. "Be careful – don't knock anything," whispers Amma. But she's more likely to do that than I am, because she's going to have a baby. The room feels like a musty old museum. There are big oil paintings on the walls of dead things and glass domes on china columns with dried flowers arranged inside. In the corner, a big glass cabinet between them, there are two white marble statues of naked ladies bending over shyly, in modest poses, as if they've been surprised to be found in such a state.

"Come and sit by the fire," says Mrs Cheney. "Especially you, Gerda. You need to take the weight off your feet at this stage."

"Mary, do take their coats."

Mary bobs, "Yes, ma'am."

She seems very old to be called by her first name. Amma always calls Mrs Smith who comes and cleans by her full name, never by a first name. She must have one but we don't even know what it is.

"And you can bring the tea."

Abba gets up to help her when she comes in with a large silver tray, and Mrs Cheney puts out her hand. "It's alright, Wasi. Thank you, Mary. That'll be all. I'll ring if we need anything."

Mrs Cheney twinkles in the firelight. She's a little plump woman who sits up very neat and straight, like the Queen. We all sit up straight as she does, sipping cups of tea carefully. Mary has brought a glass of milk for me.

"A terrible thing, this famine," she says. "Very shocking. I remember when Billy and I were in India how upset we were by the state of the poor people."

"Very bad," agrees Abba.

I think of the picture in the encyclopaedia.

"Naseem, dear... This is very boring for children... Mary!" She rings her little silver bell. "Take Naseem into the garden so she can play. And when you go home, don't forget to remind me that I've got something nice for you."

We're all very dozy with politeness and cake when we leave to drive home. I sit on the leather-smelling seat at the back clutching the book on birds I've been given. "It was one of my son's favourites." The place is like a big doll's house I saw once in a museum, I think, with Mrs Cheney stuck in it, as a little peg-doll, trapped. I don't think she can ever get out. I imagine her sitting there for ever, like a clockwork figure, sipping her cup of tea very delicately.

"A very good woman," says Amma.

"She's been very generous to the India Famine Appeal."

"But a pity Billy couldn't be there."

Yes, I'm sorry too. Mr Cheney whom everyone calls Billy and never 'Mr Cheney' is such a jolly little man with his white hair and his red face. He always pretends to box when we meet and then he cowers back as if he's waiting for me to give him a knock-out blow saying "Don't hit me!

I surrender!" He has a big factory, says Abba, and is a 'rough diamond' which means, I think, they are very rich.

"Do you think she's lonely?" asks Amma.

I stop listening because I suddenly remember the dancing now and the real band in their uniforms, quite clearly, even though I was very little. When I heard the music I just needed to dance, and so I did. I remember how surprised I was when people sitting around having tea started clapping. I had no idea why. They stopped when the band went on and I just went on dancing, and I was glad about that because it was just for myself and not for them. But thinking back, all that was only baby dancing. What I really want to do now is what all the girls at school do, and that's learn how to tap dance.

"Amma," I call out. "I can learn tap dancing, can't I?"

"We've talked about it."

"Yes but—"

"Not now. We'll discuss it later..."

"Don't upset your mother," says Abba firmly from the driving seat, and that's that.

But 'later' goes on and on. Months go by but I do not forget.

I catch Amma when she is making *puris* in the kitchen. Usually I love watching her doing that. She drops a spoonful of batter into the pan with hot oil and it hisses like a dragon or a snake. She waits a bit till it goes brown and then she presses the puri down under the surface with a big kitchen spoon. The puri puffs up. It suddenly changes from being just a pancake and turns into a balloon.

But I am not bothered about puris and balloons today. I am on a mission.

"Why not? It's not fair!"

Amma sighs, "Not again...!"

I don't care. I can't think of anything I've ever wanted more than to learn to tap dance. All the other girls go to classes every weekend. They show each other bits of what they learnt when we're in break in the playground. They go clatter-tap-tap on the tarmac and I'd so love to have a go. Barbara Clowes invited me home one day and showed me her tap shoes. They are so beautiful – bright red and shiny like apples, with little spotted bows on top. I stroke them gently. "Go on, you can try them on," she said, but I don't want to. I want my own.

"So why can't I go to tap classes? Give me one good reason. Just one!" I insist.

15

Amma is not sympathetic. 'You know what your father said. And keep away from the hot fat.'

"Well, *why* won't he let me? He's just being *mean*."

'And you're being selfish,' she snaps. I gasp. My mother has always taken my side. How can she let me down? It's not fair! Does nobody care for me? Just then there's a wail and Amma snaps off the gas. "Now look what you've done. You've woken your brother." She leaves a pile of *puris* cooling on the kitchen table.

I want to kick something but can't see anything.

There's so much I want to say, mainly "stupid baby". Actually I've done her a favour. She should be pleased Anwar's awake at all. He's a round, fat baby, the colour of Cadburys dairy-milk all over, even his big fat bum. And he does nothing but sleep, and sleep and sleep. Everyone mentions it. When does he ever wake up? From time to time, they send me out to take him for a walk and Abba's patients who come across us crowd around his big high pram and coo. "Isn't he a beauty? And so good! Fast asleep, bless him." They don't know sleeping's all he does. Amma jokes about it. "He's never awake whenever people come to see him. I can see them thinking I must drug him!"

He is no use at all, none. He's too young to play. I'm not allowed to dress him up, and anyhow I'm nearly eight and well past the age for dolls. And all the fuss over him! And he's done nothing to deserve it. But he is a boy.

When the doorbell rings, it's more visitors. "Well done, Wasi," say the doctors from the Indian Association. Dr Sethi, Dr Prem and Dr Singh arrive first with their wives and clap him on the back. Even the teachers at school have heard and they congratulate me. "You must be really proud of your little brother!"

"Yes," I agree. And I explain solemnly, "It's good because boys are more important for Indian families." I know as I say it that I am being mean, even meaner because I pretend I'm not. I wish they'd say that I'm wrong or how bad that must be, but nobody does. And then I feel even worse.

But little by little I begin to see Anwar's got something. He sits up, he tries to pull my hair and he's cuddly – round and fat as butter, with big dark eyes. "Ooh, those eyelashes," gasp the patients – on the rare occasions when Anwar is awake. "I'd *die* for them, wouldn't you?"

When he starts to talk, he calls me 'Seem' and I don't mind showing him how to build things with coloured plastic cups, and reading him Beatrix Potter stories. But I am seven years older and there's a limit, and anyhow he's fussed over by loads of grown-ups – there's Amma and Mrs

Smith and masses of Abba's patients who decide they want to take him out in his pram, as if he was the first baby to be born in the world. One of these 'Aunties' brought him home all flustered yesterday. "I didn't know where to look, Mrs Khan," she told Amma. "One of Doctor's patients stopped and wanted to have a peep at Anwar. When she bent over the pram, do you know what – he spat straight in her face!" I thought it was very funny. And then Liesel arrives from Germany to be our live-in help, and she's yet another person to fuss over him.

She's short-tempered and moody. Something really bad happened to her in Germany but I don't know what. Abba and Amma say I have to be very nice to her. "Why?"

"Because..."

Liesel can't speak any English, so she and Amma chat all the time in German. They sit around and grate little hills of raw potato for *Kartoffelpfannkuchen*. I watch it as Amma drops a spoonful of the mixture into a hot frying pan where it spits and sizzles. "Your grandfather could eat twenty-one of these at one sitting!" And they cook bratwurst and a weird knobbly vegetable called kohlrabi. They chat all the time, non-stop. I just hang around and no-one pays me any attention and then one day I notice that I can understand what they're saying even though it's in German. It's almost all clear, even the swear words. It sounds like the kohlrabi – knobbly and crunchy and inside full of goodness. I listen hard and wonder if I'll find out why Liesel is cross so often. It's something to do with the war, and people she calls 'Polacks'. "Sorgen," she says when I ask her why she has those lines all across her forehead. I pretend I think it means 'frowning'. But I know quite well what 'sorgen' means. I just don't want to know.

And then Abba decides I ought to know Urdu too. He points to the milk jug at breakfast and says "Doodh." And then he points to the table and says "mez," very slowly. Then, "Say after me: alif, be, tay..." And then he realises it's late and he has to go to the surgery and that's that. Later, when he remembers, it's 'doodh' all over again. So we never get very far at all. I can talk about milk jugs and tables, but in German I can talk about sorrow.

He doesn't get the importance of dancing either, and that's what I really truly care about. "You're like a dog with a bone," says Amma crossly. "Drop it."

"Is it because of being Indian?"

"Ask your father."

So many things seem to be not allowed because they are 'not Indian'. I can't have a dog because it's 'not Indian'. I can't have my hair cut because it's 'not Indian'. "No, it's got to stay in plaits," he says. Every morning Amma pulls them tight and I shriek. And I can't learn to dance because... There's no-one I can talk to about it. Everyone at school's English and they seem able to do whatever they like. They can tap dance and have short hair and as many dogs as they want. Hundreds of dogs, if they want.

The Indian Association people are the only other Indians in the whole of Birmingham and we only see them once a month..

It's coming on for summer, and an Indian Association Sunday.

"Gerda, Naseem, go and sit in the car," Abba shouts. "It's time to go."

"I'd better stay home," Amma says. "Anwar's going to wake and need a feed."

She helps me put on my cardigan and I go and sit in the car and wait for Abba.

"I'm just coming," he says and disappears. I wait. There's no sign of him. Finally I get fed up and go back into the house. "What's he doing?" I ask. "Goodness knows," Amma replies. "Probably gone upstairs to wash his hands again, you know your father." It's true. We've spent hours in all, just sitting in the car, waiting for Abba to appear. We never learn. "Go and sit in the car..." and we always do.

At last he comes down "Why aren't you in the car?" and we set off. The Indian Association meets in a different place every time. We never know where we are going to go. Today it's a long drive through quiet Sunday areas in the back-streets of Birmingham, past Small Heath and Bordesley Green. "There's the mosque," he says at one point and I look for an oriental building with domes like in my Encyclopaedia, but it looks just like an ordinary terrace house. Rather shabby, in fact. We go through bits of Birmingham that I've never been to before and I'll probably never recognise again. If Abba dropped me here, I'd be like the babes in the wood. Eventually we draw up outside the gates of a big school. Abba drives in and parks in its big empty playground. The building looks deserted and shut up with that sad look of a school when there are no children around.

"Come along," and I tumble out. Abba's already halfway across the playground, greeting people, and into a side door. The grown-ups are busy in the main hall setting up and trying to make it feel not so much like a school, as if the teachers are going to come in any minute to take Assembly. Some of the younger doctors are setting up tables round the walls, and arranging seats in rows facing the stage. The older men are just standing around chatting noisily and it echoes. It sounds so bubbling and excited – and it always does, even though they see each other every month.

I move towards the little crowd of wives at one end who are busily taking containers and tiffin carriers out. A faint smell of spices is slowly overtaking the smell of chalk and school polish. I hang around but none of the other children are here yet. Usually there's a crowd of us. I wish Amma was here, but she doesn't really like Indian Association events: "It's all backbiting and politics." But I do, and I love the Christmas party when Dr Majmudar dresses up as Father Christmas (because he's the tallest of the doctors) and all the children get brilliant presents.

I can see him over the heads of the others, and Abba bouncing up and down talking in, I suppose, Urdu and certainly not about setting up tables. Someone taps me on the shoulder. It's Mrs Barnabas. "Your mother not here?" She sends Dr Barnabas off to join the men and pats his hand fondly, her pale hand looking very white against his black one. Dr Barnabas is the blackest person I have ever seen, perfectly black, black as a blackboard, and with a perfectly white moustache and twinkly eyes and wobbly tummy when he laughs. I imagine he could make his patients feel better just by laughter. And he seems to make Mrs Barnabas happy too because her eyes are always smiling.

At last, some other children arrive. Here are the Shankarayyas, with two boys around my age – Uma and Chandra – and their older brother who's already studying to be a doctor. We're all going to be doctors of course when we grow up. I hang around Mrs Shankarayya feeling shy and secretly want to stroke her sari that's silky and glowing orange and bury my face in her large soft bosom. I think she is the most beautiful person in the world, so soft and calm and slow-moving, her thick black hair in a large bun at the back of her head. I wish Amma was more like her instead of sharp and busy. When I get near I can breathe in a sweet smell of face powder and something spicy I can't name. But it's lovely. She'd never get cross, I believe. I'd like to stay here forever.

But she's taking a set of food containers out of a basket.

"Now you children go on and play," she says absently, waving us all away.

"Come on," says Uma, "Let's leave them to it," tugging at my hand, "And look, here are the Sethis."

You can't mistake the entry of the Sethis.

"Come along, Sethi!" comes the clear high voice of Kay Sethi. She cuts through the crowds in her high heeled way, clip-clip. There's a little fox fur curled over her shoulders with strange glassy eyes. Dr Sethi follows in her wake like a shaggy kind bear. I don't think she's brought anything. Anthony – my best friend out of all the Indian Association children – slides away from them. I can see he's relieved to get away. Amma says he's very good-looking and I suppose that's right, but more important he's not a goody-goody like some of the others. "We'd better hang around a bit and be polite," he groans. And we let the grown-ups pat us and ask how we are doing at school, but mostly have to just listen to their talking to each other – all about the cost of new cars, new houses, children's school fees and how well we're doing in exams. And then there's politics, like Amma said, especially today because there are elections. That must be why Dr Majmudar is here. He doesn't come to Indian Association events very often. Mostly he entertains in his grand house in Handsworth where he has an Alsatian dog called Prince and a bright green parrot. But here he is today, chatting to Dr Prem who's wearing a chain as the President until they vote for a new one. Finally we are told to go off while the grown-ups have their meeting. "Come on," shouts Anthony with relief, and we shoot off.

The school is a great place to play. It goes on and on, with miles of corridors, and half a dozen of us race along them; we peer into classrooms and play hide and seek, shouting and banging on doors. Then Anthony discovers a way into a second playground. I don't think we're allowed to be here, but we find a way to run right round the whole school building. On the other side we find a large heap of coke piled up against the wall of the school.

Anthony looks at it.

"Bet you can't climb it!"

"Bet I can!"

I am not going to be beaten by Anthony Sethi. Uma and Chandra and Susheela hang back, but Anthony and I rustle and crunch our way, sliding back and pushing on upwards, to the top of the coke mountain. It slithers and shifts under our feet but at least it's just coke and not as grubby as coal would have been. I am panting but we make our way in unison up to the top and find we are by a high window looking right down into the hall. There are all the grown-ups – far below us, like coloured dots – seated in long rows of metal school chairs. "It's the voting," says Anthony. The men are springing up and down, waving bits of paper and silently gesturing. At one point it looks as if a fight might even occur. I had never thought that voting could be so exciting. "Does your dad want to win?" I whisper.

"No way. He's got more sense. 'Can of worms', he says. Anyhow, Mother wouldn't let him."

"Quick! It's ending," he hisses and we rustle down the coke. "Hurry up," hiss the others. "We've got to get back," and they scarper.

"Do I look OK?"

"Not too bad," says Anthony, and we brush off smudges before we go back into the hall. "I'm starving." I've lost the ribbon from one of my plaits but it's too late to go back.

The hall's different when we get there – quieter than it had seemed from our window. No-one's fighting. "Who won?" I ask Abba.

"No-one. We decided to postpone the elections till the next meeting."

Everyone starts to make a move to the food table, but before we can, Dr Prem makes an announcement,

"Dr Mehta has kindly agreed to show some of his home movies," and two of the doctors are already pulling a big projector and screen into place.

I'm really hungry now, but films could be like 'Bambi' and I sit down by Abba, but it's not like a cinema. The pictures are faint because the hall isn't dark, and there's something wrong with the sound. But as the reels whirr and the faint images pass over the screen, I sit up, quivering. I cannot believe what I am seeing. I am outraged. The film goes on and on and people around me are starting to shift and clear their throats. But I am stiff, bursting, in my metal seat. Dr Mehta is showing reel after reel of his daughter Pushpa – who is only a few years older than me – twirling and whirling and standing on the points of her toes. She is dancing! She is actually doing ballet! How can she be allowed to dance and not me! I look accusingly across to Abba but he is secretly looking at his watch. The films finally end, and there's a patter of claps and I open my mouth to speak. This is not fair.

"And now," announces Dr Prem, "Let us all sing India's new national anthem." There's a big rustle and I have to bite my tongue but not my fury. Everybody stirs and gets to their feet and a wavery line of singing begins.

"Jana gana mana..."

It's only a few months after Independence and nobody really knows the words. When we get to the chorus "Jai he, je hai..." there's a great burst of energetic singing – "Jaya jaya jaya jaya hai" – because this is the easy bit.

And no-one is at all sure when the anthem is over. They start to sit down at the end of every verse, and then suddenly guiltily get up again when it's clear there's more 'Jaya jaya jaya's' and even more of it. It seems to be very long, much longer than 'God Save the King'.

I look over at Anthony and we both try not to giggle as the grown-ups bob up and down like apples. But that does not mean that I am going to forget about my grievance. And I have evidence now...

It seems an age afterwards, and plates of food afterwards, and then tidying up. They're always very fussy about tidying up because if we leave it smelling of curry we might not be allowed to come back again.

When finally we leave, I can contain myself no longer.

We're out of the hall and on our way across the playground to the car, "Abba – she was dancing!"

I tug at Abba's hand.

"Why is *she* allowed to...?"

He pulls his hand away, "You know we've had this conversation." He opens the car door. "Get in."

"But why is she allowed? She's Indian, so why can't I?"

Abba switches on the ignition. "Abba!" Finally he says "They're not Muslim." He says it crossly as if that explained everything but I can't see it. "They're Hindu."

"What difference does that make?"

He doesn't answer.

The car makes a slight grinding sound as he changes gear as if the car is cross too. We set off home. I turn round and look back at the school, all silent now and dark at the end of its vast tarmacked playground, lights switched off and doors locked. I suddenly remember what it looked like when we arrived, only three hours before. There is no difference. I blink and look again. I am right. And I suddenly feel odd. Children coming to school tomorrow won't have any idea of what went on in their school the day before, I think. Not even a slight smell of *bhajias*. All that talking and noise and greeting and laughing, no trace of it. It is as if it is an English world and we are invisible, unseen and not part of it.

And where in this mix of Muslim and Hindu and English and not English do I belong?

CHAPTER THREE
1951

The house feels uneasy. Something's up, anyone could tell. Abba's roaming around opening and shutting drawers, for no reason whatsoever, starting to do one thing and then a few minutes later letting it drop. A bit later he says maybe he'll drive up to Elmdon Motors and have a chat to Bert Sergeant because there's a funny noise in the Lagonda.

And then I hear the sound of Abba and Amma arguing from upstairs, and I peer over the banisters.

"Throwing good money after bad..." I hear her exclaiming.

"But just listen, Gerda, just listen. Give me one moment..."

This is surprising. Abba never pleads, not ever. Abba tells, he instructs – he doesn't plead. When we go on holiday he will say something like, "I am going to Morocco this year for my holidays."

Sometimes I say with pretend innocence, "Oh, really. Where are we going to go then?" But he just doesn't get it. It's being Indian, says Amma: that's just how Indian fathers are. Hmm, bossy, I think.

But today it's different, almost as if Abba feels on the wrong foot. For once I notice how small he is. They ignore me when I come quietly downstairs wondering what's up. He's following Amma around, attempting to put sheets of paper before her. She dodges him. They move from hall to kitchen, and then to the breakfast room. It's like a game. I am fascinated.

"No," she declares, "A hundred times no!" and tries to retreat into the kitchen again. "You should have learned your lesson after the Delta."

Ah, that's what it's about!

"But Gerda," he's coaxing her now. "You know I can't do it without you. You know how much I depend on your judgement."

"Then why don't you listen to what I say?"

"Of course I listen. Why don't you just meet me halfway and agree...?"

The Delta, I remember the Delta. Even baby Anwar probably remembers the Delta Trading Company. Boxes of stationery arrived in the house, all looking very grand and official with the name 'Delta Trading Company' in gold and Amma and Abba's names as managing directors.

"This is going to make us rich," said Abba and he was busy and very happy. Every afternoon he would drive down to the new office between doing his doctor's calls.

"What do you do there?" I asked.

"Getting orders," he said, looking very important.

"Orders for what?" But no-one ever answered.

At home at night he and Amma would pore over things called invoices and loading bills together. But it ended badly and none of us got rich. It turned out that people wouldn't pay him for the things they bought, and when he asked the bank to lend him money to help, they were unfriendly. In the end I used the Delta paper for drawing on, but even so there was just too much.

"Maybe you should just stick to doctoring," Amma suggested, and at that time he agreed in a small voice.

"You're right. After all, what do I know of business? And all these businessmen, they're nothing but sharks. They're all out to take you for a ride."

And now this.

And he isn't giving up. Every day he produces new thoughts and arguments and points things out in the paper that says we are living in a boom time for Birmingham. It's as if he doesn't want to be ordinary or just a doctor.

And finally Amma is worn out. She says alright, and gives her blessing to the new thing whatever it is that will make us all rich, the Betta Jig Tool and Gauge Company. I drive down with Amma to see the office in the back-streets of Birmingham full of little factories and workshops. It doesn't look grand enough to make us rich, and it is very smelly. There's an office with a secretary but it shakes with the noise of machines that are making jigs, tools and gauges.

For a time Abba seems very happy. He hums in the morning in a tuneless way and pats me on the head as he sets off to make new contacts. He looks different from his doctor person. There's something a bit like a swagger. His happiness comes through the front door in advance of him like a warm wind and everything seems as if it glows.

"Never mind," he says grandly when Amma says lunch will be a bit late. "We'll all go out to a restaurant." This is something we never do.

And they decide that I should go to boarding school, even though it is very expensive.

"Maybe it will be alright this time," Amma says to Liesel. But she doesn't sound totally sure.

And when summer comes, Abba announces he has booked a holiday for us all. We're going to a seaside cottage in Wales for three weeks. Liesel can go to Germany for her own holidays and it will be my last holidays before I go to Roedean, so we'll have to get all my uniform before we go. Navy blue suit, gym slips, navy knickers, "and white knicker linings!" Amma exclaims as she and Liesel go over the list that seems to go on for pages. "And a cloak. Mein Gott." The cloak has a hood to it like Red Riding Hood, and I love the feel of it. Cloaks and midnight feasts and japes and best friends like in Malory Towers.

We're packing up at school, and Miss Parkinson asks us what we're all going to do in our holidays. "We're going to Wales, to somewhere called Criccieth," I announce.

"Criccieth? I know Criccieth!" Jennifer shouts from a desk near me. "Criccieth's where I go every summer to stay with my nan!"

Abba and Amma call her parents and then her Nan and it's all arranged. "You'll have someone of your own age to play with," they say. After all, Anwar is only four.

They load the car up with luggage, on top, in the boot and inside – "Bismillah," says Abba and I copy him, "Al Rahman al-Rahmin," to keep us safe and off we go. The map from the RAC has a red line running from Birmingham to Wales and I have the job of looking after it. And I teach Anwar to Spot the RAC Man. It's a great game. We all love the RAC patrolman, Abba, Amma and all of us. We never know when he's going to come roaring up on his big motorcycle and side-car. He is like a knight from the Round Table – our champion and protector. "There he is!" we shout, as he comes into sight, his dark blue uniform and his peaked cap crisp and perfect. The RAC badge is mounted proudly – like a lance – on our front bumper, and when he sees it, he salutes smartly as he zooms past. Abba nods in a noble unconcerned manner and Anwar and I cheer. Later we spot his rival, the AA man, in his sickly pale yellow uniform (so much weedier than dark blue), and we make puking noises.

"Hush! You'll distract your father," says Amma. "Anyone would think you're the same age as Anwar, Naseem." But we know Abba likes it. We're all in holiday mood, not everyday. Abba is even wearing sandals.

The RAC's red line runs all the way across England and hours later when we're tired and our holiday spirit has dribbled away, we reach Criccieth. Anwar is fast asleep and I feel like doing the same. But then Abba stops, puzzled, beside two stone pillars by a narrow driveway that leads into a thick dark wood. He hesitates.

"Are you sure?" hisses my mother. But the pillars say 'Bryn Arfon' clearly. No mistaking. He turns in. Slowly we bump down the drive that goes deeper and deeper into the wood. The further we go, the more silent it becomes. We are shaded on both sides by old trees and dark dusty rustly rhododendron bushes. The woods crackle with the occasional sound of a mild foraging bird.

"I'm not happy about my suspension," mutters Abba.

At the very end, the wood thins and we emerge to a large old stone house with a sign to 'The Annex'. But the annex is a whole cottage –with a mossy slate roof and thick stone walls. The key is in the door and Amma checks her paperwork, "This is it." Inside it's wonderful – old and quiet and full of smooth worn flagstones, little nooks and hidden doors. "Your bedroom's up there," says Amma and I go through a small door up a little windy staircase all of its own. I can hardly believe my eyes. My room is tiny and cosy. There's a bed with a red velvet cover and a real window-seat where I can sit and read completely hidden behind heavy curtains. Pine trees tap at the window. Owls hoot. Oh, how Julian, Dick, George and Anne would love it. If they were here, how we'd explore together. What dens we'd build and what adventures we'd have! I dump my bag and run down my little private staircase (my own staircase!) and up to Abba and Amma's room where they are busy unpacking. Anwar's still asleep in a corner. Abba is feeling one of the twin beds as I enter.

"This is better," he says to Amma. "I'll take this one."

She moves her case off it.

There's a knock at the front door. Visitors? Who could they be? Anything seems possible in this magic place. It's the owners – Colonel and Mrs Maxwell – who live in the big house and who have come to see if there's anything we need.

"How nice to have a child," they say and beam down kindly at me, "You must explore our gardens. Anywhere you want..."

So I do, feeling warm and dizzy with happiness, crunching down neat gravel paths beside beds thick with flowers. No-one minds me. They're all far too busy at home with Anwar who's just waking up. I tiptoe round the big house and I find enormous serene gardens and then to one side a bit full of vegetables, with real peaches trained against a warm red brick wall. Then in yet another small side garden looking out onto sea in the distance, I find the most extraordinary thing – a sort of summer-house. It turns around so its open side always faces the sun. I can push it round all by myself. I try it in different directions and then I whizz it around very, very fast and jump on until I feel a bit sick. I can hardly wait to show it all to Jennifer – wood, peaches, summer house and my special secret bedroom.

But when we ring Jennifer's Nan, Jennifer has other plans. "No, come down to the beach," she says. "I'll meet you there."

"But Jennifer..."

But she won't budge.

"Red hair," says Amma meaningfully.

It's easy to get to the beach, going through the wood and then down through the little town. I step onto the low wall and look down over it. Everything widens out – sea and sky, a big sweep of pale sand, and frilly ripples of waves white at the water's edge.. Here and there little family groups are set up around deckchairs and windbreaks. A mild breeze that smells salty is coming from the sea and I push my hair from my face. Everything is big and sparkling and quiet – the noise of the little town behind me stills – just the high sound of children mixed with the steady rhythmic swoosh of the waves. High up, gulls circle and caw.

Jennifer runs over to me. "At last! Come on," she shouts. "We're late." Late for what? She's off and I follow, the sand is scrunchy and getting into my sandals. She takes my hand and pulls me past the edge of the sea where little kids are busy digging holes for the water to run in. Past the deckchairs and a group of donkeys. Right at the far end I can see lots of bigger children playing a game – a kind of relay race with sticks: jumping around, cheering and shouting, I think that's where we are heading.. "Come on – do hurry up," sighs Jennifer. "It's alright. I'm allowed. Nana knows. It's alright."

It looks as if some grown-ups are in charge. Maybe it's a school. But it's the holidays...

"Of course it's not school," scoffs Jennifer. "It's a mission."

"A what?"

"You'll see..."

When we arrive the game's over and the children are sitting on the sand drinking glasses of squash that are being passed round.

"I've brought someone," Jennifer announces and then she walks off to sit down with the group. I feel as if I'm a fish she's just caught. The grown-ups, I can now see, aren't really that old. One of them – a tall girl with bushy hair pulled back in a rubber band, walks over.

"Hello, 'someone', I'm Maddy," she says, "Welcome. I'm sure you've got a name."

"Yes. Naseem."

"What?"

"Naseem..."

She looks dubious. "Hmm... We'll have to find something else. A bit easier. How about a nickname. Haven't you got a nickname?" I shake my head. I can't see why 'Naseem' is wrong.

"N," she muses. "N for... how about 'Nutty'? How does that sound?" She sounds pleased with herself as if she's solved a difficult sum.

If I say that I don't like the idea of being called Nutty will they say I can't stay? Maybe they all have silly names? I don't want to be called 'nutty'. Everyone knows it means 'daft'.

"OK," I say.

By the end of the afternoon I don't care what I'm called. We have the best time ever with game after game.

"They're students," shouts Jennifer when I manage to get hold of her. "They come here every summer. It's great isn't it? And wait till you see the Revered Reed..." and then she's gone in a whirl of freckles and orange hair. We have another relay race and then a game of tag, and then the students go off to fetch stacks of wood. We sit round the fire they build that crackles bright. "We can roast potatoes in it another time," they say, "If you don't mind them being a bit burnt."

"We're rotten at roasting potatoes though," says one of the students honestly.

"I'll walk with you," says Jennifer when everyone starts to go home and I'm looking for my sandals.

"Hey, Nutty," calls Maddy. "You coming back tomorrow?"

No one minds that I spend day after day on the beach, even when Jennifer's not there. Gradually I get to know the names of the students: Maddy and Jeff and Allan and Alison and a few more. Every morning they tell us what's planned for the day. "Bring your swimming togs," they say one day, "Tomorrow we'll do relay races in the water." Another day it's a scavenger hunt. We're given a list of things to find – a used bus ticket, a pink shell, a comb, a piece of string – and sent off around the town or the beach to see who can get most of them. Another girl and I spot a rubber band on the kerb and make a dive for it. "Go on," she says generously. "You can have it."

"Thanks. I've found a spare bus ticket you can have if you like."

Every day it's different – races or quizzes or treasure hunts – and I forget about the revolving summer house and the exploring the woods. But one thing is always the same. "Time to go..." and the students – who feel like big brothers and sisters now – lead us up to a small building near the sand to listen to Reverend Reed. We arrive out of breath after all the running around but the minute we go and sit down in long rows, and Reverend Reed starts to talk, it's peaceful. It's special.

"Squash up, Nutty," whispers Maddy and sits down beside me. I thought on the first day that it was going to be like a lesson.

"He's like a sort of vicar for Cambridge University," Jennifer said when we walked back to Bryn Arfon, "And he's here every summer with some of his students."

But he's not preachy or strict like a teacher. I think he looks more like a film star than a teacher: dark and thoughtful. He just tells stories. He stands in front of us and talks. I like his voice: it's gravelly and relaxed.

"That's because he's Australian," says Jennifer.

But it's not just his voice. Beside him he's got a large screen with painted backgrounds. For each story, he takes different cut-out figures and sticks them on, more and more as the story goes on. As we watch, it changes and grows almost like a film. Here's the Red Sea, and look how it swallows up the Egyptians chasing Moses and the Israelites. And there's the coat of many colours that his father is putting proudly on Joseph. Here's Moses again, and the Burning Bush. Eli in the Temple. And above all there is the figure of Jesus, so loving but so suffering.

No-one's ever told me much about the Bible before. Or not that it matters. But it does, I can see that. Reverend Reed tells stories from it as if they had happened just the other day. The way that Joseph's seven brothers are so jealous of him, "Look around," he says, "Don't you see people being mean every day?" And there is my favourite Ruth who loves Naomi just as if she really was her mother and then has to decide if she'll stay with her or go back to her own country. And the disciples, one after another leave whatever they are doing and set off when he calls them, and follow Jesus. No question. They just know in their hearts it is right. "What would you do," asks the Reverend Reed, "If Jesus came and asked you to follow him?" He means it. He's not just saying it. And he waits for us to think about it, for it to sink in.

They're more than stories. He's talking to us – he is talking to me – directly, quietly and seriously about real people faced with real questions and challenges. They have to choose. What should they do? What is right? What would *you* do, he asks, if you were there? But what does it mean to be 'right' or indeed 'wrong'? When they're cross with me at home it's because they say I'm being naughty, but I don't think that's the same as being 'wrong' but I am not sure how.

Behind Reverend Reed the badge of the Scripture Union hangs on the wall. It's an Aladdin's lamp with rays springing out from it: gold on a dark green background. The rays on the left are for boys and the ones on the right are for girls, he says. "If you take Jesus into your heart, another ray will go up on the lamp..." Every day the rays grow. Days go by. I watch the rays go up.

"And how about you, Naseem?" asks Reverend Reed gently after some days. "What about your soul?"

I don't know what to say. I feel frozen. I can feel kindness coming from him, wrapping itself round me like a warm blanket. It is astonishing, confusing that he cares about what I think. A soul? My soul? I've never for a moment considered I could have a soul. Nobody has ever told me I could make my own choices either. I am only just twelve. People tell me what to do.

It makes me uneasy too that a grown-up is taking me seriously, as if I am a real grown-up person. That he is urging me to look deeply into myself and to see... what? God? Jesus?

God is not in our lives at all in Rowlands Road. We are Muslim, says Abba, and we have Allah; Abba goes to the mosque and we are not allowed to eat bacon. And of course I'm not allowed to have a dog or learn to dance. But we like Christmas and Easter eggs and they are Christian, aren't they?

I thought he might go away, but Reverend Reed doesn't let me off the hook. I feel his waiting. And suddenly I get a flash, something stirs. I remember in the summer running along the pavement on my own and the soles of my sandals smelled rubbery in the heat and all the trees were big and shady and for a moment I felt happier than I had ever felt before. I felt as big as the world but also happy being who I was. Everything was holding me warmly. It felt like the world was a big warm animal and my skin had turned as soft as a young apple and I could actually feel the vast all-over animal breathing. Was this God? Maybe it was.

And I think of my German grandfather, and our trips to see him on his birthday. Everyone always came to his little flat to see him and wish him happy birthday – his friends from the pub, the players in the local football team, even the mayor. He was respected by all, said my mother, because he'd always fought for justice. I could see it. The way he lived. A small flat. The streets outside black with coal-dust from the mines. Inside, not too much of anything, just enough of everything. Simple, but just right. It was called having a conscience, said my mother.

And the children who've saved people – the boy who put his finger in the dyke and stopped the sea rushing in; Grace Darling who rowed out in the storm to save the sailors even though people told her not to. That was the 'right' thing.

Yes, I think. And another ray goes up on the lamp and the girls all cheer.

It's been another particularly good day on the beach when I walk drowsily back along the long tree-shaded drive to Bryn Arfon. When I get back to our home, Abba is sitting there waiting for me. No Amma. I know immediately there is trouble.

He has found the Bible that I keep by my bed. He slaps it down on the table and shouts,

"What's the meaning of this?" in a voice like thunder. Next he picks up the notes that go with it for daily readings. "And this...?"

He is very angry.

I swallow.

"I'm a Christian," I say. It doesn't come out very loud but it is enough.

"A Christian?! You are most certainly not. You are Muslim!"

Next morning we are up early and he drags me down to the beach to confront Reverend Reed. I protest. I dread the thought of the confrontation. I am going to be shamed up in front of everyone. But there's nothing I can do about it. He's walking quickly and everything that looked so wide and cheerful yesterday feels as if all the happiness has been squeezed out of it. I have to run to keep up with him, and his silence is dreadful. "Now show me where you go," he says abruptly as we reach the beach. I mutely point out the Scripture Union building with its sign – 'CSSM Children's Sea-Side Mission' and he looks as if he's going to pull it down and stamp on it. He storms in and demands to see 'the man in charge'.

Reverend Reed deals with Abba calmly but seriously. "Why don't we go somewhere more quiet and talk it over?" he suggests, leading the way up the headland. The climb takes some of the heat out of it. Finally we reach a cliff top overlooking the beach and the silent sea. But Abba is still ready to fight.

They don't fight though: they argue. Abba and Reverend Reed. At first they argue about me. But then it seems as if I have been forgotten. I sit on a large outcrop as they pace up and down, Reverend Reed and my much smaller father, and this time they are arguing – it seems – about who made the world and who saved the world. "How could God have a son?" I hear Abba snort as if it's a very stupid idea, and they are off again up the rise, back and forth, this way and that, Abba fighting for Islam and Reverend Reed for Christ. "Ah hah!" Abba exclaims in triumph at one point as if he has just given a telling blow and wags his finger, and to my amazement Reverend Reed laughs. Slowly it looks to me as if they are actually enjoying themselves.

And what about me and my soul? They seem to have forgotten about me. "He's a good man. Intelligent. But he's on the wrong track," Abba says aloud, as we go back home, walking more slowly this time. I'm not allowed to go back to the beach but it doesn't really matter because we are going home in just a few days.

At night in my little secret room, I look out at the dark wood and wonder about it all, the argument and the business of a soul. What does it mean? I think it is that I should make my own choices – like Ruth and the disciples, or like grown-ups do. I don't have to be what they tell me I am. But then if I am not 'Naseem', what am I? I am not sure if I can manage this. It's too difficult to think about now. And in just a few weeks, boarding school. I say a prayer to Jesus that he will be with me there. I back it up by Allah.

CHAPTER FOUR
1952

I t is very quiet in our big communal study room. Just the scratching of many pens. Except for mine. This is letter-writing day and I've hardly written anything. In fact, I am stuck.

Dear Abba and Mother, I cross it out and then start again, writing 'Dear Abba and Amma' instead..

"I hope you are well. I have had a cold, but I am better now. Everyone here is coughing and sneezing. The weather is very wet."

So wet. When I looked out of our shared bedroom I could see rain lashing all wet over the playing fields and the sea over the edge of the cliffs glinted with big clouds passing quickly over it.

"... So we didn't have to do games. We had gym instead..." The balls in the gym were hard rubber ones and bounced dangerously round and would hurt if they had hit. I do not write this. My pen's running out of ink and slurps rudely when I refill it from my ink well. Nobody looks up. All around me, the others are scribbling away, heads down, at our weekly letter home. They seem to be writing pages. What can they be writing about?

"Thank you very much for the parcel. I shared the sweets with Fuzz. They were wizard..."

What I'd really like is some of Amma's *gajjar halwa*. Moist and chewy and oozing with richness. Only three weeks to go to half term. It feels a long way away. Home feels a long way away.

"Five minutes more," says the prefect who's sitting at her desk on a little platform so she can see we're not talking or mucking about. "You'd better start ending your letters now."

"We've got a film this evening. I think it's about the war. 'The Dam Busters'. I am looking forward to coming home. Will you collect me from Victoria? Love to you and to Anwar – tell him to be good – and to Liesel and give baby Helene next door a special kiss for me.."

I stop and then I add, *"PS Could you send me my blue dress with a sash belt?"* The red one with smocking at the front they sent with me is far too babyish. Some of the sixth formers even wear nylons and high heels when we have Saturday House Dancing.

Someone rings the bell with a deafening clang and immediately people start to get up, banging desk lids and chattering.

"Quiet!" shouts the prefect. But she's not one of the strict ones so no-one pays her any attention. It's free time and everyone's pairing off into their sets or with their special friends. I search for Fuzz's wiry black hair over the crowd.

"Boring! Glad that's over for another week," she says cheerfully. "Coming up to the room?"

"No, let's go out."

She makes a face. Fuzz hates out.

"It's really cold." And I know she's managed to smuggle a copy of *True Confessions* for us both to read.

"It's stopped raining. And I've got to pick up a book outside the Rat's room." She sighs. "Alright. Get my cloak for me, OK? I need to go to the aunt."

"I'll meet you by the Bunny Run."

The Rat has signed *Sue Barton Student Nurse* to show that it's fit for me to read, and I leave it by my locker in the smelly Boot Hole for later. I'd better remember to collect it or else I'll get ticked off.

It's bells and rush all the time, not at all like Enid Blyton and Malory Towers. Bell at seven to queue outside Matron's room so she can take our temperatures to make sure we haven't transported any nasty bugs with us from home. Bell at eight for breakfast – "You didn't pull your bedclothes back so they can air, Naseem," says Matron who can't pronounce my name and always calls me 'Naarzeem'. – But nobody can pronounce my name – I've even had to come clean about being called 'Nutty', and that's me now for another six years. The prefect on duty comes round after breakfast to make sure our rooms are tidy. Then it's bells again, for lessons.

Which lesson in which room, what to wear – shorts or tunics or afternoon dresses or navy blue suits for chapel twice on Sunday. Don't run, only walk or else get a ticking off. I don't think the girls in Malory Towers or St Clare's ever had so much that could go wrong. I've worked out all the slang now, but at first I didn't know what people were talking about. We have to call every teacher 'Madam' which is easy but of course they all have nicknames like 'the Rat' for Miss Ratcliffe. I've got it now. 'Bate' is for temper, 'bish' for a mistake, and 'aunt' of course is for the toilet. No-one, it seems, has midnight feasts. I wonder if Enid Blyton knows that?

I find Fuzz and we struggle out along the main path. She was right – it actually is rather cold. The wind off the sea just over the playing fields makes our cloaks swirl around us and we have to shout to make each other hear. This really was not a brilliant idea.

"OK, just once round the roller-skating place. It'll be more sheltered there..."

We make our way down past the playing fields, with the San and the Junior School to our left. "Or we could go to Spiders?"

"No point. Nobody's going to be on the Downs."

That's true. When it's good weather Spiders is brilliant. I found it by accident one day by squeezing into bushes behind the Chapel. They go right up to the boundary fence and there's a hollow where you can sit and be perfectly invisible and see ordinary people – families and couples walking up the Downs – and even hear their conversation. Nobody has any idea that we are there. We eavesdrop on little snatches of their lives and then they're gone again, back to their homes and to tea. In the distance you can even see Brighton, all glittery.

"Come on, can't we go back now?" Fuzz complains.

"Oh, OK, feeble. How about going to see Charlie? She brought a tin of drinking chocolate back from her folks."

"No, didn't you know? She finished it and the Muck found the empty tin in her woppee-b and gave her such a jaw!"

Wow, our house matron, Muck, must have a special antenna that lets her nose out anything we do that's not allowed. And to go poking around in wastepaper baskets, like being a spy.

"Only another three weeks and then we can have as much hot chocolate as we want," Fuzz says snuffily.

"Unlimited."

"And chips."

"Together?"

"Don't be nutty, Nutty."

I make to hit her but she ducks. At least that warms us up.

It's a relief to get back into the greater shelter of the side entrance of the Bunny-run that leads unofficially by the dustbins into our own House. "A film tonight," I shout over the tail end of the wind, "The Dam Busters".

"Oh boring... At least I'll get and see good films at half-term. Dad's screening 'Marnie.'"

"Lucky you, a dad who owns a cinema. All I get are free pills."

"And it's my cousin's bar mitzvah. That'll be fun." She pulls the door shut against the wind with a bang and we pause to get our breath back.

"Not as much fun as Jewish weddings though. You should see them – all our relatives looking out to see who they can pair off next."

"Sounds like Indian weddings. Is that's what's going to happen to you?"

"I suppose so. How about you? Will you have to marry a Muslim?"

I remember to pick up 'Sue Barton' as we head for the warmth of our shared bedroom – free till the bell for tea. "Well, I was supposed to marry my cousin Iqbal but I think they've gone off the idea. My mother put her foot down, thank goodness."

"Was he good looking?"

"He writes really boring letters from Pakistan all about being top at school."

"Oh, yuk."

However when I am finally home, two unexpected things happen.

We're driving together, Abba and I, like old times before I went away to school, when he's doing his afternoon house calls to patients who can't get in to the surgery. Most often he wants to take me in to introduce me.

"They'd like to meet you," he says. "Come in and just say hello..."

"Do I have to?" I'd rather sit and read while he does his visit.

"And after that," he goes on, "You can wait in the car."

He picks up his leather doctor's bag and leads the way briskly to the front door of a small terrace house. In the front window, flanked by net curtains, there's a statuette of a little girl holding out her wide skirts.

Abba is treated like royalty. He knows everybody in the family not only the woman at the door, but her children and her parents. "Doctor delivered me," she says proudly. "And is this Naseem? Hasn't she grown! I remember her when she was just a little thing."

"She's at Roedean," he says. "One of the top schools in the country, you know."

"Goodness. And what do you want to be when you grow up?"

"She wants to be a doctor," he answers for me.

"You must be very proud, Doctor."

We drive around the area, from Yardley to Sparkbrook from visit to visit and then over to Balsall Heath: different houses but identical streets and identical houses. Rows of them, one street after another. They look as if they've all been run up at the same time by a gigantic sewing machine: neat cramped terrace houses with bow windows. Same respectable scrubbed doorsteps. Same little girl posing in the front window. Same front gardens edged by low brick walls. The sameness is predictable.

But then I realise there's something rather odd going on. Normally

Abba's a cautious driver. Normally he drives at around twenty miles per hour. But today he's almost speeding. We are seemingly tearing along the very streets where he normally dawdles. I grasp the side of the car and then, when I look out, see something I've never seen before. It's Indians but nothing like the Indians I've known for ever through the Indian Association. These are poor Indians, wearing un-English clothes, floppy cotton trousers that look like summer trousers with suit jackets on top and on their feet – in this weather! – sandals. They change the streets and make them look different – foreign, exciting. English people don't stop and chatter or sit on steps and gather round front doors. What are they doing here? But Abba looks to neither right nor left. He must have noticed, but he is putting his foot down and speeding on at this unnatural pace.

"Abba, stop! Look! Who are they?"

He tuts irritably and doesn't answer.

"Go slower, I want to see..." But he won't.

I wind down the window.

"Shut it," says Abba abruptly, and signals turning right. "*Gundee*," he mutters. He is talking to himself, not to me. We leave the Indian-peopled streets. I crane round to look through the back window, but we have left them far behind and finally Abba slows down to his normal speed.

"Village people," he says dismissively. "They don't even know how to use toilets."

"Which villages? Why are they here, Abba? Where have they come from?"

He won't say any more.

But others in the Indian Association have noticed the new arrivals too and they do have something to say.

"It's shocking, isn't it?" says kind Mrs Barnabas sadly, "All these poor people in such sub-standard accommodation."

"Better than they ever had in their villages," says Dr Rao in a huffy sort of tone.

"It's a bad show," another doctor puts in. "It's all the government's fault. They're letting the wrong sort in. It'll lead to trouble.."

"Well, I can't see it matters," my mother declares staunchly. "We need the labour. It's 1953, not the days of the Raj any more." They look at her as if she's a talking dog, as if she's mad. She turns and stalks away.

But in the car on the way home she explodes. "Ach, such hypocrites! I couldn't stand it! They're just so stuck up! So full of themselves with their big houses and their big cars. And now they're afraid English people will think that they're the same as those people who 'can't even use toilets'. Instead of coming from a country that's full of maharajahs and... and elephants!"

And then the second thing happens and that's even more surprising than newly-arrived immigrant Indians.

It's a Sunday morning and I'm in the kitchen with Amma. Abba calls out, "Naseem... Come into the front room. I've got something to talk to you about."

"Go on," Amma says. "I'll join you in a minute."

We don't usually sit in the front room, it's where Abba has his roll-top desk and where they entertain when visitors come.

"Sit down," he says when I slowly make my way in. He is smiling but in a way that doesn't look quite real. "We have some exciting news."

Amma comes in, drying her hands, and perches on one arm of the sofa. It feels as if they have rehearsed a play together.

"You've always said how much you'd like a sister. Well, a girl called Shamim is going to come to stay, from Pakistan."

"She's going to come and live with us," my mother corrects.

"All the time?"

"Yes, for good. Now, you are going to be really important because she's never been out of Pakistan before, and she's only a bit older than you."

"She is your half-sister," says Amma.

"Yes, but we are not going to say that to everyone."

A sister... a real live sister. It's like a school story, something by Enid Blyton. How wonderful.

"When's she coming?"

"In a month."

"But I'll be back at school.."

"She'll still be here when you come home."

"Can I tell Fuzz?"

They look at one another.

"Better not right now."

"She can share my room if she likes."

Shamim rhymes with Naseem – it sounds like Enid Blyton's Terrible Twins. How wonderful I'll have someone to do things with in the holidays. Nobody from school lives anywhere near. Fuzz lives in Thames Ditton which is miles away, and Anwar doesn't count.

"She's a very serious student, very clever. She wants to be a doctor," says Abba.

That's not so wonderful. I do hope she's not cleverer than me. Every time my school report comes there is such an atmosphere and I feel quite sick. If I'm not at the top of my class Abba gets angry and threatens to take me away from Roedean and send me to the secondary modern and not waste all that money. What if he takes her round to visit patients instead of me and says "Let me introduce my clever new daughter."

"We don't know much more," Amma says. "But we'll all find out soon enough. In the meantime, let's get your things together. We need to pack for going back to school."

Back at school, I mark out the days until the one when Shamim is due to arrive, When it finally comes, I wait for my weekly letters from home. Abba's letters are rather dull and he often dictates them to his secretary who types them. But I can rely on Mother who always writes lovely newsy chatty letters. She tells me all about the classes she's going to and the funny things Anwar says, and she is sure to tell me everything about Shamim. I am dying to know. But this time she doesn't write, just adds kisses to the end of Abba's letter. And Abba doesn't have much to say. He just writes very briefly that Shamim has arrived and is *"very tired"*.

So many weeks to go! I am consumed by curiosity, and tell Fuzz but swear her to secrecy.

"You're so lucky!" she whispers after Lights Out. "All I've got is a dog."

Another week goes by and then at long last a letter, and such a fat-looking one. Mother's energetic writing on the front is unmistakable. I race upstairs with it. Now I'll know all about it.

It is not what I expect.

"Well, Naseem," she starts. "Shamim is here. She arrived two weeks ago. And she is," and the next word is underlined, "Awful."

I gasp. I read on. There are pages.

"She's small and fat and very stupid. And she speaks hardly any English. She sits and sits there day after day and does nothing but *grins*. Like an ape.

"She has no ideas of her own at all. If I suggest things that she could do, she just says, 'As you wish' to everything."

The paper on which she is writing is jabbed as if she has attacked it with her fountain-pen, and her large writing dives across the page like gunfire. The force of it makes me feel breathless. And confused.

I know Mother doesn't have friends, or family in England. There's no-one she can really confide in. Part of me wants to hear all this, it's like gossip or Fuzz's True Confessions magazines. And I am secretly pleased that I am still the best; but part of me wishes she didn't have to tell me all this. I don't feel old enough. I am only thirteen.

And what next? No-one tells me that, even though I ask and ask when I write home. Term ends and the summer holidays begin and there is no sign of Shamim when I go back home. She has gone to a residential college to train as a nurse, says Abba shortly. No, she won't be back for the holidays. She'll stay there.

Nobody will speak about her and Mother never mentions the letter she wrote. 'Good riddance,' is all she'll say. Only six-year-old Anwar volunteers that he liked her. She was nice. She'd spent a lot of time with him, playing with him, he said. He'd taught her the names of all his Dinky cars and she was really interested though she wasn't good at remembering, he said. She couldn't even tell the difference between a Hillman and a Ford.

CHAPTER FIVE
1959

We are walking, Abba and I, up and down the vast and empty recreation grounds at the back of our house, Yardley spread out below us in all its uniform tapestry of sameness, when he says, out of the blue: "I've been thinking... Why don't you change your name?"

"What?!"

Abba likes to walk in a particular way. It's a duty rather than a pleasure. I believe I can hear him counting the number of times he needs to cross the park for the sake of his health. We walk smartly from one end of the featureless grass – not a flower bed, shrub or tree in sight – to the other. Then, wordlessly, he wheels round and goes back the way we've just come. It is like being in a walking army.

"I've been thinking. You could easily pass as English. And it might be easier when you leave university."

We turn about again.

"In fact, I've even thought of a name for you." He stops and, with the modest air of a conjuror producing a rabbit, asks, "What do you think of... 'Julia Masters'?"

And then he catches sight of my face.

I am outraged. I dislike the name 'Julia' anyhow and I think 'Julia Masters' sounds like a failed librarian, but above all how could he take away my name, my birthright?

"Only testing you," he says rapidly with a totally false little laugh. "I was only testing you."

Just because I don't look Indian.

I know that. And I know that my name gives people problems, or seems to, and the fact that I am not one thing or another. I am sick to death of people asking, even when I was at primary school, 'Which side do you identify with?' as if only one side can be the real thing. Why do I need to choose? Why can't I be both? It sounds as if Abba doesn't think that I can. As if he is chucking me away. Maybe he thinks I'm not the genuine article too?

"And I hate the name 'Julia'. I can't stand it."

"No need to get hot under the collar," he says soothingly. "It's just talk."

Of course, he is thinking of prejudice.

It's hard to get Abba to talk about their early days in England. He prefers to talk about success – the houses he owns, the cars he possesses – rather than hardship. And when I look at little black and white photographs with other young Indian students they look so larky and cheerful in their over-sized winter coats and jaunty trilby hats. But just occasionally, if I am very smart, I can wheedle him into memories.

"Things must have been so different when you and Mother came here," I muse. "You know, when I was born, there were only one hundred Indians in the city. And now..."

"Many, many. Well over two thousand," he agrees. "When we came here, I don't think any of my patients had seen a brown man before."

I risk a direct question,

"Wasn't there prejudice?"

"No, not at all. In fact I remember," and he starts to chuckle, "Before I came to England, one of my uncles taught me how to read hands. He said that English people believed that Indians had magical powers, and every pretty woman would want me to hold her hand and tell her fortune."

We both laugh.

"And of course, being here in Birmingham was lucky. Just an accident."

"What do you mean?"

"I must have told you..."

"Told me what?"

"Let's sit down a while. I'm a bit tired."

We find a bench that's overlooking the view.

"No, I never meant to," he resumes. "I was doing a locum in Birmingham for a few weeks, I forget the name of the doctor, an Englishman. Your mother and I were saving very hard so I could buy a surgery – this was before the National Health Service – and I was taking on locum work here and there all round the country.

"After completing my visits one day," he warms to his story and taps his stick on the ground in front of him, "I stopped by Woolworths to purchase something. When I entered the shop, I suddenly heard a great cry, a big commotion, everyone running this way and that. The shop manager had collapsed on the ground!

"Now luckily, I had my doctor's bag – I would never leave it in the car – and I stepped forward. I could tell straightaway what the problem was and could prescribe there and then."

"You cured him?"

"He recovered. And then, this," he taps me on the knee, "This is the point. He asked my plans and he said he would lend me the money on the condition I stayed and practised in Birmingham."

It's like a storybook.

"But," I venture, "Didn't you ever want to go back to India? Not to live, but just to visit? You haven't since I was, what? Six years old."

"India, Pakistan, what's there?" he says abruptly. "Poverty, bureaucracy, law suits."

He looks at his watch, "It's getting late." He pulls himself up with his stick and stands for a time looking around at the windswept rec and the grey-white vista of Birmingham. "That was a good talk," he said and turns toward home, "I need my tea." Julia Masters is forgotten.

The phone is ringing insistently when we get back to the house.

"It'll be the same man," announces Mother crossly from the kitchen. "Another one who can't speak English. How they get by, I don't know."

"Abba wants me to change my name," I tell her as we start to make tea.

"He gets these ridiculous ideas. I hope you didn't say yes?"

"What do you think?"

"It's all because he couldn't work as a surgeon." She is rummaging in a cupboard for a tin of biscuits.

"What do you mean?"

"You know," putting digestives out on a plate, "It's what he really wanted to do. All that time in Edinburgh doing his FRCS. Get the kettle, will you, it's just boiled. But in those days no-one who wasn't English could get a look in, however hard he tried. Discrimination. White people only."

"Is that what the extra case is? The one in the cupboard under the stairs, next to his doctor's bag?"

"It's his surgeon's case. He won't let it go. '

"That's awful!"

"But he's had a good life as a GP. All his patients love him.' I know that, but I can't dismiss the image of the unused bag under the stairs.

But our talk on the rec must have stirred something because when I am back at college, a few weeks later, I get a message to call home urgently.

"How would you like to come to Pakistan?" he says. "The marriage of your cousin, Nafees, is taking place in May..."

Now that's a better suggestion than Julia Masters.

It's like a blast furnace. The light, the impact, the noise of it. It smacks

43

me between the eyes the minute we leave the shadowy crowded railway station. Bang – the brightness of Hyderabad. No shade, no refuge. My eyes sting with it and even Abba blinks a bit.

No-one else seems to mind at all. We are surrounded by a crowd of men who all seem to be relatives of some sort – I never knew I had so many – and the overall level of excitement is very high. Our arrival is a big event, an occasion. Even people not connected with us stop and stare. Here is Abba, important in his 3-piece Western suit: the fabled son who decades ago went to the West – way before anyone ever except the very rich – and now has returned. We've been garlanded and greeted, and there's a lot of what strikes me as muddled running, organising transport until Abba insists no, he wants to ride in a tonga – "Naseem would like it," he says and he is actually quite right. I do. Since there's no room for anyone else in the tonga they decide to use the limousine that's now appeared and we set off. My head is spinning with the crowds, the language, the shouting, the brightness and the sheer wonder of it. And how must Abba feel? It's over ten years since he was here and that was before Partition, so it was still India, not this very new Pakistan.

It doesn't get any less intense as we sit, the two of us, regally, in a vintage carriage pulled slowly by an equally vintage horse. The passing scene is amazing. Our old horse ambles along through the most chaotic traffic I have ever seen. Big lorries decorated with pictures of roses, waterfalls and snowy mountains swirl around us. We look down from our tonga's height onto little auto rickshaws that dash and swerve in and out of traffic. The hooting is constant– not restrained little tooty English-style horns, but big rubber horns like the ones that clowns use in circuses that rasp away assertively and always to any purpose. It is as if everyone is shouting their existence with a burst of ferocious exuberance.

"This is wonderful – I love it!" I shout to Abba and I clutch the side of the tonga and lean out. Abba doesn't look nearly so enthusiastic and I begin to think he might be regretting his choice. He has now donned dark glasses and I can't read his expression. Although at first it looked grand, the tonga has seen better days: it has no springs, no suspension. Our ride is very bumpy. We can't recline or loll – just grit our teeth and we bounce along. But who cares? Life around us is so compelling.

On either side of the road life is being lived in greater variety than I could ever before have thought possible. There's clanking and banging from small auto-repair shops. At the edge of the road two men are welding, the sweat running off them, and the sparks flying out and fizzling and cracking. Every inch of ground is filled with some enterprise. Vendors sit cross-legged on the ground shielded from the sun by large black umbrellas, their wares spread in front of them. Men push mobile stalls mounted on old bicycle wheels. We pass a cluster of vast drainage pipes waiting to be installed. A family appears to be living in one of them. The smoke from a small brazier makes the air above it quiver with its heat.

"The smell!" I shout to Abba – food stuffs and gasoline and singed hot dust and at times the unmistakable acrid smell of open drains. Abba takes his white handkerchief out of his breast pocket, knots it and places it on his head.

It takes an age of rocking slowly through the streets – potholed wide carriageways and the little bazaar-like streets crammed with open shops vivid with neon strip lighting. And when the horse stops, I am almost lulled into a sense of time just going on for ever and ever.

Nor can I, for the life of me, see any house. Just shop after shop, and shops that are just apertures raised up and open to the unpavemented street, their owners sitting cross-legged on the platform edges, at the mouths of seemingly brightly-lit caves.

But between one cave selling stationery and another stocked with bales of cloth, there is a barely visible large wooden door, reaching way up to the shops' first storey. In the middle of the gate there's a smaller postern door into the hidden family house behind. This is 31 Tilak Road, the family house after Partition.

Abba pays the tonga driver and I can see that he's been given far more than he ever expected. For an instant, there's a flash of the old patrician who saluted the RAC man on the road. But quickly gone because we are awaited and are drawn into the house, and the chaos of the street abruptly ceases. The walls are thick. The house must be very old. It is tucked away behind the bazaar, arranged around an internal courtyard that's open – two storeys up – to the sky. Right now the courtyard is crammed. The reception party from the station is all here but now the crowd includes women – "I'm your auntie," says one large woman and then another and they both hug me – and a very large number of big-eyed open-mouthed children. More garlands – fresh marigolds, all damp with water to keep them fresh, orange petals interleaved with strands of shiny tinsel. The aroma is subtle, delicious.

"Take it off," Abba mimes discreetly and demonstrates. Ah, it's not done to keep it on... What do I do? What am I supposed to say? Slowly it becomes clear that I am expected to detach myself from the male group round Abba and our luggage, and follow the friendly auntie. Her hand is warm and plump.

Seats are brought out into the tiled courtyard, and Abba is seated in pride of place, handkerchief and dark glasses now removed, and more and more people come to greet him. He is excited, ebullient. What must it be like, after all these years to be back in the heart of a family – a big clustering throng – rather than our neat two-children family in the edges of grey Birmingham?

"Aare baap, this can't be Mehfuz/Ijaz/Salman..." I can't catch the names and there are just too many. "You were only just so high last time..."

"Yes, yes," they admit shyly, and there's happy laughter all round as they are pushed forward by other relatives. I am slowly starting to sort them out – the first I have ever really had. Mother's sister, Aunt Else in Germany hasn't got any children. Anwar and I never had cousins on tap or aunts or grandparents. But now I have scores of Pakistani relatives, wherever I look, and even more will arrive for the wedding itself in a couple of weeks' time.

Even better I have two girl cousins more or less my age – Nafees Fatma and her sister Anees Fatma. Their middle name comes from their aunt – Abba's much loved sister who has died. And that's why I am Naseem Fatma. Oh joy, no-one here finds my name at all difficult to pronounce or weird. They say it (not Julia Masters) with a musical lilt that is quite, quite different from the way the English do. It makes me feel curiously graceful and swan-like.

"We've been so longing to see you," says Nafees with the sweetest of shy smiles and I am immediately smitten. She is slight and exquisite, dark almond eyes in a heart-shaped face. She and her younger sister, bouncier Anees, they say, live in the upper part of this house. "Your Abba is our Chacha," Ah, my father's younger brother, Sami. "Those, over there," Anees points them out, "Are our brothers."

Both girls, I see, are wearing shalwar-kameez, with veil-like dupattas over their long dark plaits. I try to straighten the folds of my green sari that's got crumpled in the tonga. I can see no other women in saris.

"And where's the bride?" calls Abba jocularly. "She's the reason we are here..." Of course, it is lovely Nafees. Older women push her forward and she tries to pull away and looks embarrassed. "Come and greet your Chacha," says Abba expansively. "We've come a very long way for your marriage."

"And the groom!" exclaim several voices.

"Maqbool!" commands his father. And a bespectacled youth comes forward equally sheepishly.

"This is very modern," says Abba and it is not clear if this is a criticism. "In my day, bride and groom never saw each other before the marriage."

Times change, everyone agrees. "Nowadays young people have a voice."

"It would be difficult for them not to meet," whispers Anees to me, "Since he lives downstairs."

"You don't mean you're first cousins?"

"Yes, his father is Mujtaba Chacha over there –" she points out a dignified older man with a sharp pointed white beard. "He was married to your Abba's sister, Auntie Fatma who passed away. They live on the ground floor here, and we live upstairs."

"And Iqbal," I remember I was promised to him originally, "He's the older brother of Maqbool?"

"That's right. But of course Iqbal bhai lives in France now."

"But is it alright to marry your first cousin?"

"Of course. It's our tradition."

"In England..." If I had married Iqbal who clearly is my first cousin then I would have been Anees's sister-in-law and her first cousin too. And my uncle would also have been my father-in-law. And does that mean my father would also have been my uncle? It feels very tangled.

Cold drinks in glass bottles arrive, and snacks, and then Abba is asked what we would like to eat.

"No, don't take the trouble. We are booked into a hotel."

Several people look shocked and raise an outcry.

"Surely not, after all these years!"

Uncle Mujtaba – who has the sober gravitas of a committee chairman – raises a hand.

"Let him do what is best. After so long in the west he's used to certain comforts. They can spend every day here with the family." There is a bit of muttering, and Anees-Nafees whisper,

"We wish you could stay here with us. Can't you?" I'd like to, but a large group comes to escort us to our hotel and we are borne away.

In the air-conditioned quiet of the Sind Hotel – the best they say in Hyderabad – when our escorts have slowly departed, Abba starts to deflate. He shakes his head,

"Too many people. I'm just not used to it any more."

"Anees said why didn't I stay in the house."

"If you'd like to... See how you feel tomorrow. Take rest now. I'm tired. I need to lie down."

I stop at his bedroom door, remembering something that puzzled me.

"Abba... When you gave everybody their presents, nobody said thank you or even opened them."

"Correct behaviour. Good manners."

I don't get it.

"It's not..." he searches for the right word, "Dignified. It's not dignified. It's like children, making a fuss over being given presents." He mimics a child, "Ooh, look what I've got!" He switches off the side-light. "The giving is important. Not the gift."

Another thing to learn. Like garlands. Like saris. And a few days later, with Abba's approval, I move to the upper floors of Tilak Road.

Downstairs, Uncle Mujtaba and his sons have two bedrooms with proper beds and a rare wonder, a bathroom with a flush toilet. But we live in a more old-fashioned way upstairs and I am very glad for it. There's hardly any furniture for a start. Rope-based beds – charpoys – are pulled out at night and Uncle Sami's sons sleep on the flat terrace outside. For the rest of us, sleeping mats and bedding are pulled out of big old cupboards and we lie down to sleep where we are, in our clothes. "Will you be alright?" asks Auntie Khurshed in Urdu via her daughters. I am fine. More than fine. I like the sparseness of it. In the daytime, the rooms simply change character, not bedroom but sitting room and not sitting room but dining room. At mealtimes, a tablecloth goes down on the floor and we sit and eat cross-legged around it. I am enchanted. Why on earth have different rooms in the west for different functions? Why have so much cluttering furniture? Let's be sparse, fluid, stretchable.

We are a lot of people up here – six children and sometimes two more arrive by Uncle Sami's other marriage. He keeps himself to himself. I pass him sitting on his charpoy in the Pakistani shalwar that he always wears – unlike Uncle Mujtaba who's in western suits. He's a big rumpled man with bloodshot eyes, and a sense of untidy uncaring powerfulness that makes me feel shy. Every morning he goes out to do the shopping – women, I gather, don't do this here. At mealtimes, he slurps up his dhal and curry silently with one hand, nodding tersely to his wife when he wants his plate refilled. He does not speak English.

I have never experienced a life that is at one and the same time so spacious and yet so constrained. Nobody – at least, not the women – goes out, or if we do it is in groups, shepherded and protected by male relatives. People – women – come to us, climbing the stairs turning their heads away as they pass Uncle Sami reading the Urdu paper on his charpoy. In our quarters they chuck off their concealing black burqahs, loll against plump cushions on the floor and relay news of the outside world – scandal, gossip, countless family feuds.

Time is fluid. In the morning, the sky is pearly and big with crows. Even the bathroom is a fascination, though it makes Abba shudder. It's a long room with a line of raised supports. We squat companionably crapping side by side. Early in the morning a shadowy figure slides in through a side door and removes the product.

There is a lazy unforced quality to life – we pore over film magazines and plan new outfits and I jettison my saris. There is nothing like fashion or labels or boutiques in Hyderabad. We make up our outfits piecemeal from big Butterwick catalogues and they are made up by an elderly tailor who arrives with his sewing machine balanced on his bicycle's handlebars. But time goes by and I start to fret. I look out of the high unglassed windows open to the jumbled rooftops of Hyderabad with their strange wind-tunnel towers – 'Special to Hyderabad' – and I want to go out and explore, I want to see the shops and the street life and find the vendors whose different street-cries float up to us here upstairs.

"Can't we go out for a walk?" I suggest to Anees.

She is startled. "I think all my brothers are busy."

"But can't we just walk round the block?"

She is uneasy. "I should ask Abba and Amma.."

But he is out and she is at her prayers. I coax her. "We won't be out long..."

In the end she yields, because I am a visitor and older than she is. Outside we turn a corner and another, and then she panics. "I'm not sure where we are. We'd better go back." And we do. We creep back upstairs, avoiding Uncle Mujtaba.

At lunch later, Uncle Sami says something abruptly to Nafees in Urdu, nodding in my direction. For a moment I am afraid he knows I persuaded Anees to go out. But no.

"Abba says he would like to give you a sari." And the youngest son is sent out to bring back a selection of lurexed saris for me to choose.

And then one day – four days before the marriage – a bombshell. I've been out with Abba and when we come back to Tilak Road, the house is oddly quiet. I look up at the balconies where Uncle Sami's family lives. Not a sign of life. Where's everybody? Uncle Mujtaba is sitting there on his own in the courtyard, reading his English language paper.

"The marriage," he says, "Is off. Let them do what they want." His newspaper rustles: he turns over a page. "The gentleman upstairs," he says shortly, "Is creating trouble. Let him stew in his own juice. He is nothing but an uneducated man."

I hasten upstairs and find Anees-Nafees in the inner room. I expected an uproar but neither wants to talk. Finally, Anees explains. "It's the *meher*. Abba doesn't think it's enough. He has forbidden the marriage."

"How can he? It's only four days away!! But what's this *meher* anyhow?"

It's the amount, she explains, that a groom formally pledges to give to the wife if the marriage fails. It gets registered at the mosque. It's sort of legal.

"But wasn't it fixed before?"

"Yes, but Abba's thought again." He thinks Uncle Mujtaba is being cheap.

"I'm not surprised," sighs Abba when I tell him. "They cannot get on, those two. Bad blood." It strikes me now that they do live entirely separate lives. I have never seen either visit the other.

The atmosphere upstairs and downstairs is equally adamant. Uncle Mujtaba is curt and disdainful. Upstairs Uncle Sami sits cross-legged on his *charpoy* in his rumpled shalwar, brooding. His thick greying hair stands up like a parrot's crest and his eyes look full of rage.

"What will happen?" I ask.

Nafees looks very pale,

"It's as Abba wishes," she whispers and I have to strain to catch her words. There is something dignified about her stoicism. In the west we'd rail and rave. I think I would.

"But all the wedding clothes and the jewellery and the invitations and the cooks coming...?"

"He wants my best..."

"Well, what happens, happens." says Abba philosophically. "There's nothing we can do."

Two days, three days pass. I can't stand the tension and go back to the hotel to sleep.

Then suddenly, I arrive one morning and it's all changed. There's a huge bustle of activity, people running between upstairs and downstairs, calling out between storeys, deliveries arriving, Uncle Mujtaba's phone (another sign of his modernity) ringing constantly. The wedding is on.

"Look, there are the wedding cooks," Anees points out as we hang over the balcony – a group of men bearing huge cooking pots and sacks of foodstuff. Other men are putting up strings of electric lights. Piles of crockery are delivered and stacked in one corner. Uncle Mujtaba's cane chair is tidied away, and more and more sacks, bags and implements arrive.

More women arrive too and gather upstairs. One woman takes out her henna kit and spreads it out. "And now the haldi," says another. They rub turmeric and oil into Nafees' arms and face until they have a golden glow. Her eyes are heavily outlined with kohl. The henna woman paints an elaborate pattern on her outstretched hands and little dots above her eyebrows. "Now don't move," she instructs. I hover around, wishing I could do something. The female activity is intense. And most of the chatter is in Urdu with an occasional burst of song that, from their giggles, I think is rude.

Nafees sits motionless while the henna paste dries. She is decorated and dressed. Women cluster round her, putting on her jewellery, arranging her hair. "Look, shabash!" they call, holding out a mirror, but she doesn't look up. And then the bridal outfit, traditional scarlet gharara – very stiff – and a concealing red dupatta totally over her head and face. With each layer Nafees becomes more and more silent. When the Qazi from the mosque arrives with selected male relatives to ask her agreement, he has to ask her twice since she can't speak any louder than a whisper.

Shouts and cheering and the sound of a band announce the approach of Maqbool's wedding party from the mosque when it is still a few streets away and now here they are. Crowds of relatives and friends flood in and jostle and push Maqbool along into the courtyard. He is wearing a new dark western suit with furry astrakhan Jinnah cap. His face is obscured by strings of flowers but I can still see his spectacles glinting behind them. Abba signals to me to come down and meet people but there's such a hubhub it's impossible to hear who I am meeting,

"I'll tell you what's going on. Stay by me."

And here comes Nafees escorted downstairs, supported on either side as if she can hardly walk on her own. She looks so unreal, quite unlike the girl of yesterday and there's a hush. Her mother and two more older women steer her and Maqbool onto gilded arm-chairs where they sit like waxworks, Nafees's head bowed and her face invisible. One woman ceremonially passes a Qu'ran over their heads.

"Ah, if only my sister was here today," says Abba. "This would have been her duty as mother-in-law. And to do the rice. Mother of the groom always feeds the bride with a spoonful of sweet rice to show welcome."

Now Maqbool is allowed to glimpse Nafees's face in a mirror that is strategically nudged under her veil, as if it she is a surprise. One smart alec makes a loud remark in Urdu and everyone laughs. Anees suddenly darts forward and picks up Maqbool's shoes.

"She's his sister-in-law now, and he has to buy them back," shouts Abba to me over the laughter. Everyone gets into the spirit of it, like a bidding auction. "Five hundred rupees," calls Maqbool.

"Too stingy!" people yell. Everyone claps and they chant, "More! More!" He struggles on, trying to snatch them back but she hides them behind her back. The pots bubble and the smell of food and spices – chicken biryani, basmati and spices and creamy sewaiyan – rise up. Children run around in wonderful finery, many that I've never seen before. More relatives. I am introduced to my Aunties Zakia and Akhtar who look like big glittery cushions, all soft,

"Your father's famous, you know. He was the first to ever go to the West."

"And he never forgot his family."

More cousins, aunts and uncles.

The party goes on for three days, and Abba and I admit defeat at one point and go back to the sanitised quiet of the hotel.

Finally it is all over. We stop by at the quiet house on the way to the station. The courtyard is cleared, the relatives have gone home. The monitor lizard that vacated the space during the hullaballoo is back on the wall.

Khan Sahib is at the mosque, says a servant. Upstairs, Nafees is ill in bed – "nervous exhaustion," diagnoses Abba – and Maqbool has gone back to his job in Karachi. "Allhamdullah," says Abba and we take off.

Bismillah Al Rahman Al Rahim.

In the name of God, the Most Gracious and Most Merciful.

Back in Birmingham, we drive through the mean streets of Sparkbrook and Balsall Heath and I sigh. I miss the unapologetic colours, the little parrots at sunset and the call to prayer that punctuates and anchors the day. I miss the cocoon of family, the long hot afternoons in Tilak Road.

"Write," urges my cousin Anees, and several others. "And come back."

I have a family now: I have filled in some of those empty outlines. Abba is silent. The evening is drawing in, and the traffic lights blink glumly in the wet streets.

The future looks drab and troubling – finals around the corner and then out into the world with no idea of what to do with an English degree. The safe predictable life of a protected Pakistani daughter looks inviting by contrast. What do I have to look forward to?

And then when – by sheer chance – I visit an old school-friend, a young man, a friend of Val's brother, looks at me and glows like a sunbeam and he thinks my name is beautiful. And I realise I am wrong about a drab future.

CHAPTER SIX
1962

We are walking along the busy Euston Road, David and I. I still can't believe it. I try the words out in a cautious stumbling way, as if the words might slip out and bite me on the tongue for my effrontery. 'David and I', 'David and me', 'we'... He is easy and happy, however, and has no such problem.

"I've got to collect some things from my folks' place," he shouts above the traffic. "OK to come along? We don't need to stay long."

His folks? For a moment I worry that I'm not dressed properly. I haven't met his family and surely taking someone home to meet parents is a big step? But then David's Australian and free, it seems, of any old world angst.

A few months only since that magical day at Val's and London has become transformed. When I slink off illegally from Oxford, hoping I will not run into a don on the train, I find a different London from the London I know of train terminals. I am taken to the Courtauld Gallery at the top of a faceless building in Gordon Square, and see its earthy Gauguins. I drink espressos in a left-wing coffee bar near Chalk Farm and watch foreign films in the National Film Theatre. I am in the dazzling British Museum where David stands me in front of Japanese celadon pots. "You can tell when it's good work, you can feel a sound resonating in your belly. Try it." I watch the pot carefully and try hard to feel a resonance. I believe if I wait, it'll happen. I believe.

When he won a national scholarship to come to the famous Slade art college, his family decided it would be an adventure for them all too. And that's what they did. How footloose, how free. Not for an instant can I imagine my own family doing that. His father took up a post as press attaché at the Australian High Commission. "Mother's a writer so she can do it anywhere." And there are two sisters.

"Are they here too?"

"Yeah, but Annie's a nomad. Nobody knows how long she'll stick around. You can never tell with Annie. Anyway, don't worry – you'll like them," he says reassuringly.

We take a detour down Park Crescent because he thinks it is beautiful and wants to show it to me. It starts to rain lightly. "Not far now."

Around a few corners we come to a small mews. Stopping before number 11, he lets himself in with his key.

"Hi!" he calls out as we climb the narrow stairs.

"David? Is that you? I'm right here," a voice floats down.

In the kitchen at the top, we find his mother. She is sitting on a chair with – unusually – her feet in the open oven.

"Hello dear, that's a nice surprise," she says placidly and doesn't seem at all nonplussed.

"This is Naseem," he says. "I've told you about her." He puts his arm round me proprietorially. I am tucked under his arm and feel small and precious.

'Yes, dear," she says absently, getting up from her oven-comfort and slipping her feet into slippers. "I'm really not used to the cold yet," she explains to me. "In Melbourne it's the height of summer..." It seems a very sensible way to keep warm to me.

"You'll stay for supper, won't you? It's nearly ready."

In my world I ought to be polite and demur. But this is the new world.

"Dad around?"

"He's just got in. They're arguing about an exhibition at the Tate, I think. He'll be glad to see you. Go on in and tell them food is nearly ready."

"Maybe Naseem – have I said it right? – can help me? Ask your sister to clear the table, David dear. It'll need to be pulled out. And your father'll need to do something about his papers."

"Well now..." she says and turns to the matter of plates, cutlery and glasses. "Never enough knives in rental places," she says tutting. "Never mind, we'll manage..." I like her. She has a warm contented way that makes me feel at ease. I like the place too. The sitting room is small but full of books and newspapers and deep sofas. There are a variety of people whom I can't quite work out but all seem friendly as I come in with a tray of plates and salad. When we finally sit down to eat, it's on an assortment of ill-matched chairs, around a big pan of lasagne. From time to time the door-bell rings and other Australians turn up. "No worries, we're not stopping. We just thought we'd call by to say hello," and they perch on the side of armchairs and join in the conversation and periodically drift into the kitchen to help out or scrape the pot.

I sit scrunched up between David and his younger sister Frannie and listen and wonder at it all. It's all so easy, so comfortable. They talk about new exhibitions and films they've seen or want to see, if they're on the side of someone called Brett Whiteley or Sid Nolan ("that old fossil!") about the vagaries of the Tate's policy, the best options for travelling round Europe, where to find Vegemite. They share news of friends in common and banter and gossip. No-one seems to mind being challenged or contradicted. It's all taken with extreme good humour.

I find my plate being automatically refilled by someone, I don't see who. It doesn't matter.

This is how families ought to be. "Hush," Abba always says. "Don't talk. Just eat your food." I think of Birmingham and our shiny neat house flanked by rose beds like a spiky Praetorian Guard. But here it is all sunny uplands. And normal. They're so interested in each other, so at ease with one another: parents and children and friends of children. And David – lovely David when I steal a glance at him fills me with a hum of quiet pleasure.

And this continues for weeks and then months. When he first ushers me tentatively into his own place at the back of Swiss Cottage, I am entranced by its sparseness. It's one room, large and light, in a house that once belonged to a Victorian painter. Now it doubles as David's studio and living space. It's full of the pungent smell of turps and oil paint; in one corner a small functional kitchen, a mattress on the floor, his few clothes hung up neatly and not much else. He pulls the single chair out for me – "Sit down," as if I am a special guest – puts on a kettle to make Japanese matcha tea. When it boils, he pours it out into small pottery cups that he made and fired himself. The walls are full of his sketches, and he pulls out even more drawings and etchings from a wide flat drawer. "Take this," he says, "And this..." and presses them on me. I sit there with quantities of art spilling out of my hands. I feel like the Queen of Sheba, showered with largesse. He wants to share things that he finds precious with me. "Take this..." he says. We kiss. Very gently. It is as if we are both holding our breath. Here. I feel that I am in the place I had always wanted to be.

This is love, high octane love. Trees bloom out of season, cats smile at me in the street: even the rush of London traffic seems to skim by on smooth and silent skates. I sneak off to London whenever I can, even though university rules forbid leaving Oxford. I arrive at Paddington Station and look for his blond smooth head over the crowds, waiting for me at the barrier. He is always there.

A message in my college pigeon hole tells me my mother called and I should ring home. She wants to come up to Oxford, she states – there's a new development concerning Shamim. No, I think silently. Go away,

Mother. I don't want to hear it. I am in a cloud of happiness and I don't want it to break.

"I've got an essay to write before the weekend..."

But she insists,

"I'll drive over to Oxford. I'll take you out to tea. You need a break."

Shamim, I think, as I slowly cycle down past Carfax and the High. I remember how thrilled I was when I first learned that I had a sister. It was as if all the school stories I ever read had come to life and I was in them. A sister! Someone to share things with – gossip, confidences, troubles with parents, sistertalk. "You'll get on really well," Abba had said confidently, always believing what he wanted to believe. Always. When Shamim finally arrived – eight years older than me, tongue-tied and shy, with poor English and well, just unreachable – I didn't know what to make of her. Nor she of me.

Back when I was thirteen years old and at boarding school, I knew nothing about all the scenes that had gone on when I was away. I never knew then that Abba had left a first wife behind in India – his first cousin – and a daughter. All I knew was that when I came home again from boarding school, there was no Shamim. Not a trace. Mother looking grim but satisfied, Abba evasive.

"She's at college, and doing very well..." was all he would say. I didn't press him. I didn't want to.

I can't tell from Mother's face when we meet up in the café near Christ Church if her news is good or bad. She looks edgy but with a sort of nervous, anxious energy. She won't settle at first.

"Impossible to park," she complains. She fiddles with the clasp of her big red handbag, takes her cigarettes out and then puts them back again. She looks over at the young blades hunched over a chessboard in the corner. How unusual, she comments, to have chessboards in a café. It is small talk and we both know it.

When tea and scones arrive, she finally takes a deep breath. "Well, your father was up in London last week. He went up for the day because," she starts, "He was hoping to get some business from the Pakistani High Commission in Knightsbridge. For the Betta." She stops to light a cigarette. I wait. "He knew that Shamim worked there."

"But I thought she was a nurse...?"

"That's another story... No, she's working as a telephonist, on the switchboard. Of course, you know your father. He didn't want people to know his own daughter was working in such a menial job – and he was meeting top people in the High Commission. He'd have lost face. You know what your father's like. But he told me he'd known Shamim worked shifts so he thought he could come and go in her lunch hour without her knowing anything about it. At least that's what he said.

"He was just leaving the building when apparently she came back on duty and looked out of the window and saw him. He said she called out and when he didn't turn round, she ran downstairs. She ran after him along the street, calling, "Abba! Abba!"

I know that street in Knightsbridge – select and silent, with chauffeurs buffing limos outside rich flats.

"And then what?"

"Nothing. He pretended, he said that he didn't hear her and he just walked on. He said there was nothing else he could do."

There's a silence. Neither Mother nor I can break it. The image of a child running after a parent – a father who cuts his daughter dead – is just too shocking. It makes us both wince.

"He was very upset..." Mother – who's been at odds with Abba for months – has even been shocked out of her hostility. "In the end, he gave up. I asked him what he did and he said he went to Euston station and came home. He was close to tears."

I look out of the window at the graceful towers of Christ Church College across the way and at the confident students hanging round chatting by the porter's lodge. The evening is coming on and light is fading. Poor Abba – he is not a bad man: just tangled up by history and circumstances. It is a small tragedy, peopled only by casualties, from start to finish. The first wife, Zebunissa, left alone when Abba first came to England – a widow in all but name. And poor Shamim. Why did Abba ever bring her over when her mother died, I want to say. Why not leave her ensconced with all the cosy aunts and cousins and the family warmth I had known in Hyderabad? But then, the cause goes way deeper – to the old custom of first-cousin marriage. It is intractable. There are no winners.

In Christ Church, bells ring sweetly and surely for the hour. "Oh, is that the time?" says mother hastily, looking at her watch. "I've got to get back. Your father will be wondering where I've gone. I want to be there when he gets in."

I sit in the café for some time after she's departed. She has not touched her scones.

"How was I supposed to know? Anyone would think that SW4 was next to SW3. It makes sense... Don't laugh!"

"But you're the Brit."

'Not the Londoner." Clapham hasn't turned out to be next to Chelsea. I thought it had to be. "You've got to agree it makes sense. Who dreams up these stupid post codes anyhow?"

At the other end of the phone, David just laughs. "Come on, it's not that bad. You'll all be OK."

"It's fine for you with your folks in Regents Park and your own place in Swiss Cottage. But I seem to have got Pat, Lisa and me stuck out in the sticks. We agreed I'd find a flat for us after college. I told them I knew London!"

"No need to make such a song about it," David goes on with a touch of weariness, "Listen. We need to talk. There's something I need to tell you."

"I'm going home this weekend. Can't it wait?"

There's a slight pause. "Sure."

I can spot other people at the station by now who are going back 'home' for the weekend. We all come back on the Sunday evening train with a mildly pampered glow, fattened up and carrying bags of foodstuffs and clean laundry.

Mother, as I expect, is in the back garden, half hidden behind ranks of beans. She's busy digging and doesn't see me for a moment but then straightens up, "Ach, these midgets!" she exclaims, slapping her arms. The big vegetable plot looks so fertile.

"It looks wonderful."

It's burgeoning, full of produce – beans and peas and a covered strawberry patch and vast sprawling marrows.

"Yes, it's done well. My beans are really good this year. You'll take some back?"

"With pleasure."

"Go on in. I'll come in a little while. I just want to stake these up. Your father'll be back soon."

Abba picks up the mail on the side table as he comes through the front door. "Ah," he says with satisfaction, opening one.

"Good journey?" to me.

"Gerda." He calls as she comes back into the kitchen. "Good news. I've heard from the Muslim Burial Council. They've confirmed our plots."

She puts down her armful of earthy carrots with a thump. "You're not going to put me in a Muslim grave? You know I'm not a Muslim. I won't have it!"

"Well," he says with something like a smirk. "You won't be able to do anything about it, will you?"

She opens her mouth. But he's right.

"Ach..!"

He beams.

But she rallies. "And, that.. that thing," she points at a figurine that is new since I was last here. "That can go!"

"What do you mean?" he asks innocently.

"You know perfectly well what I mean. I won't have it in the house. You can put it somewhere else – anywhere – in the garage."

"But it's art, Gerda."

"It's disgusting."

"I thought you like art."

'It' is a bronze statuette of a very muscled naked man holding a club. His genitals are discreetly hidden by a slight bulge of cloth.

"It could be Hercules," I offer. She doesn't care. "I won't have it on display. What would people think?"

I'm not sure who wins in this exchange but for sure both – especially Abba – look brighter for it.

"Now," he says briskly and turns to me. "This flat of yours. I'm glad you are sharing with your two university friends. I need to come to see it. Are you sure it is in a safe area? At night-time?"

Incredibly safe, quite suburban in fact. Clapham, not Chelsea. Our neighbour even complimented us on our domestic skills when she looked though our window and saw how we dried our baking pans. It's that sort of place.

"But you should be saving up for your own property. This is the time. How much are they paying you at this publishing house?"

"£12.10s a week."

"Hm, you can do better than that, Oxford-educated. When you get back, go and tell them you need more money."

"Abba, I've only been there three months."

"Or do you want me to call them? I know you. You never speak up for yourself..."

Luckily the phone in the hall rings

"Get that, Gerda."

"Yet another one," she grumbles. "Don't they understand this is your home? They're not in Pakistan any more."

Abba looks weary, but he goes to the phone.

"It just goes on and on," she says. "Never-ending."

"Is it alright? All this National Front stuff, I've been reading about it.

There was a march in Birmingham the other day, wasn't there? It didn't sound good."

"Oh no, just a few rabble-rousers. They're trying to stir things up now there are so many more coming over."

"She's asking about the National Front," she says to Abba as he comes back into the breakfast room."

"Nothing to worry about," he says confidently. "The English like fair play. They won't be swayed by some hotheads."

"That's just what I told her," Mother agrees.

But there's more to it, I feel that. There are starting to be more and more talks about controls on immigration, about limiting numbers. There's a Bill being discussed in Parliament. Surely it has to be a worry?

"It won't come to anything," Abba says decisively. "Labour will win the election next year, and they won't support controls. Mark my words."

I do forget about it when I get together with David. He's borrowed his folks' Land Rover and we drive to Epping Forest where he parks in the middle of an empty glade. But he doesn't make a move to get out.

"Listen, I've something to tell you."

He pauses. "My tutor at the Slade was asked to recommend someone to be a teaching assistant in Maine at a summer school... And he's recommended me."

I start to say something but he stops me and carries on. "I think I ought to go. It'll be good for us to have a break. It's for just over two months."

He's right. The last few months have not been easy between us. Perhaps we've been too close and need air. But I find I am crying.

"Don't try to change my mind," he says looking straight ahead. We look out at the foliage that is dripping after rain.

"Do you want to walk?"

I shake my head.

Nor does he.

We drive home.

Back in Clapham, Lisa and Pat are reassuring. It's a good thing, they both say. All relationships go through dips. And two months will pass in no time, wait and see. They both cancel their dates and we cook a large bowl of pasta and have an evening in and they pat me gently. Perhaps they are right,

"Best thing is to keep busy," they say sagely.

"How about looking for a new job?" suggests Moira who's the art editor at the publishing firm where we both work, and the best thing in the little firm, "I happen to know that Fabers have a vacancy."

"Have you told your organisation that you need to be paid more?" asks Abba when he phones some weeks later.

"It's alright, Abba," I say airily, "I've got a new job. I'm going to be working for Faber and Faber. And I'm earning more money." And I've signed up to learn typography and graphic design in evening classes at the London School of Printing, but that's enough for the moment.

And David is missing me, he says. He's writing from New York on his way to Maine. "There are no trees here to go and sit amongst and be told, 'What's the matter with you, man?' So I have sat on my bed and thought of you. You are the most reassuring opposite to this town and me at the moment."

"Told you so," says Lisa.

Then, by chance, I see a small announcement in The Times, 'The celebrated dancer, Ram Gopal, is pleased to announce the opening of his School for Indian Classical Dance'. This is meant for me. I pick up the phone immediately so there's no chance that all the places will be filled.

My heart is beating so fast and I have to check myself, slow down. I don't want to be early. On the other hand – I speed up again – I don't want to be late. Everyone else here is ambling and window shopping. None of them could have any idea of where I am going and I think how much luckier I am than they are.

If I hadn't looked it up (many times), I'd think I'd got it wrong. The Kings Road Chelsea (the genuine SW3 and no adjunct to our homely SW4) doesn't seem the right place for a School of Indian Dance – or any dance school. I can tell it is very expensive, very Nancy Mitford 'U'. Very English. But what do I know? The only bit of Indian dance I've seen was when a dancer came to one of the Indian Association days; and all I remember is a stocky woman in a brilliant-coloured sari and covered in jewels doing an item that went on for ages and the doctors finally shifting in polite boredom.

But I have always wanted to dance – dance of any sort – and never been allowed to. And to combine that with India too…

There is no sign outside the terrace house in a side street off the King's Road, but the minute the door opens it's clear from the smell of incense I've come to the right place. "You can leave your things here," says a young woman of about my age helpfully. "And you need to take your shoes off. We never wear shoes in the studio. My name's Jamila, by the way."

"Naseem."

There are eight of us in the front room that's been cleared out and has mirrors and bars round the walls. In one corner there's a large bronze statue of a god surrounded by flowers. Abba would think this pagan. Just as well he can't see me now.

"We could just warm up while we wait for Ram," says Jamila who clearly knows her way around.

But then there's a flurry and a rush of air and Ram enters. He is a presence, no question.

"Very good," he says moving to face us all. His stance is marvellously upright and he looks wonderful, in a silk turquoise kurta and white churidars. "Let's get going. Let's do our namaskar." The others arrange themselves round the room and he picks up a pair of sticks to beat time.

And then he sees me.

"Ah," he stops. "You are?"

"Naseem Khan. I telephoned." I feel like saying you never told me that the others know how to dance but I would like to. I feel so stupid. I wish I'd never come.

"Ah, of course." But I am sure he does not remember. And then, "Welcome. Pick up what you can and I'll show you the steps later. You'll have to get some proper clothes though," he looks disdainfully at my shirt and jeans. "You can't sit in those..."

Sit? Oh, he means the deep plies they are all doing. He's right – I can't sit. But I'm not sure if my legs can do it anyway, even if I had the right clothes.

"This is hard work," I pant to Jamila. She is breathless too, I am glad to see.

"Come home and practise," she mouths. "And I've got a spare shalwar that'll fit you, if you like it."

It's hard on the muscles, on the concentration managing to do the exercises in a precise time measure. "No, you're too slow," he says brusquely. "Can't you *hear?*" And we all stop shamefaced. "Start again – first speed." First speed, double it, then triple it. Oh my god. But how good it feels, how exhilarating.

Classes are several times a week and I turn up faithfully several times a week with my shalwar and kurta. The moves make sense, the whole movement language makes sense. My body feels as if it is stretching, unfurling. I love it.

Sometimes we arrive on time and Ram says crossly, "You're all late. You can't be dancers if you are not serious."

Sometimes he gets bored with teaching and turns the class over to a young male senior student. Sometimes he wants to reminisce. We never know what to expect.

"It's part of the training," says Jamila when we have pot luck at her and her husband Reggie's house. "You have to accept whatever the teacher gives you."

And he is a marvel. When he demonstrates an adavu its sheer disciplined beauty takes my breath away. He is, after all, the equivalent of Nureyev. He is the man that brought Indian classical dance to England before I was born and who has danced before royalty. And now he is teaching me, in a private studio behind the King's Road.

"Yesterday we built a kiln for low fire slipware," writes David from Maine in his spiky art-school hand. *"Which reminds me that I must go and make some pots for it. It's in a big rock down near the water. God it's exciting to be doing things you love."*

"Three pages!" I say happily to Pat and Lisa, counting them over.

Time passes and we are getting better. Some students have fallen away, others joined. Just a few. We are constant pupils and begin to feel we could be dancers.

One evening Jamila's husband Reggie asks me in the breezy faux-colonial voice he favours,

"Miss Khan. Have you ever heard of one, Mr Ken Annakin?"

Not at all.

"Ah, but I imagine the name Yul Brynner must mean something to you?"

He relents and explains. Ken Annakin is a film director, who made 'Those Magnificent Men in their Flying Machines'. Now he is going to direct a film in Britain but supposedly set in 1930s India with Brynner as a bandit king.

"And they are auditioning for Indian dancers."

"Oh..." I say politely.

"So how about it, Miss Khan?"

"But Reggie," I protest. "I don't actually look Indian."

He sighs.

"Have you never heard of something called 'make-up'?"

I audition and the film company don't see me as phoney. Jamila and I sign up as dancing girls in a wedding party.

"Don't get too excited, girls," cautions Reggie who has his fingers in more pies than I know. "Rumour has it that Mr B needs instant money to pay a rather large outstanding tax bill."

"You mean we're dancing in a pot-boiler?"

"Let's just say I'd be surprised if it won an Oscar."

We turn up on Saturday to a bare rented studio above Earls Court Station.

64

"Well, at least it's convenient."

There are six of us in all.

"This is the routine," says the coach — whose name is Sheherazade — and demonstrates. It is straight out of Bollywood. It's not classical, that's for sure. We try it out. Sheherezade sighs theatrically. "You need to *frolic*," she calls. "God, these girls..." she declares to the air. Round and round we go, hour after hour. "That's it. You're getting it... Keep at it," she calls in her rough smoky voice, clapping the rhythm sharply and counting, "Ek, do..."

Smile, glitter, hips — turn and clap: smile, glitter, hips — turn and clap.

"What would Ram say?" Jamila whispers, as we dance round the room.

But Ram, I discover the next time I arrive at Draycott Avenue, will never know. "It's closed," says the elderly woman who owns the whole house sadly. "I'm very sorry. There just wasn't the demand. He's gone to Venice." We are orphaned. We look at the statue of Shiva, god of dance. The incense is still burning.

But trouble is brewing in Earl's Court. The others are all clustered round a table when I arrive. The costume designers came to measure us last week and they've brought their designs of what we are going to wear. There's a rising murmur.

"I can't wear that!" Jamila announces firmly.

"Nor me," adds Monisha.

Others nod.

The designers are cross. They've provided us with wide swirly skirts and short glittery choli tops. They can't see what's wrong with any of it. Who do we think we are — stars?

"Our husbands would never allow it."

"Look at that!"

It's the cleavage — plunging, revealing.

"But this is a *film!*"

We all stand adamant. Even I with no husband or mother-in-law. I am with them. Imagine Uncle Mujtaba or Sami seeing the film. This is my thing too. I am part of it.

The designers will not budge.

Then our coach slowly gets up from where she's been sitting, like a lion raising herself,

"Let me see." She is a pukka Pakistani woman, and tough. She knows the culture. The designers do not.

"You must do something," she says abruptly and pushes the designs aside. Her tone shows there can be no arguing. Debate over. "These girls cannot be seen like that. What their in-laws would say?"

The designers grumble but they go away and return with a compromise. Take it or leave it, says their expression. A sash, they say: to go over one shoulder and fasten at the waist, back and front. It'll totally cover everything, they say with unmistakable sarcasm.

The costumes arrive and we do our dance in the fake wedding party on 'The Long Duel's set in Pinewood. Bandit Yul Brynner bursts in, sees the chief dancing girl (parachuted in to head our dance) and abducts her. We dancing girls break off, scatter and scream, and Trevor Howard as the British Raj officer sets off in pursuit.

I go through the motions and I perform dutifully but I am not in Pinewood or fake India. As I was about to go to work this morning, I caught the postman. He gave me a letter. It's from America. An unusual stamp, I see, a special issue: a rare spotted toad. I am putting opening it off. I don't know why. ..

It starts, "This is a letter that I have tried to put off writing because I don't want to say what I am going to..." He has met a Canadian girl, one of the students at the summer school. He says he has fallen in love. He says he has asked her to marry him. He says he will always remember...

I cannot stop crying.

I cry in the breaks from filming, ignored by Yul Brynner, a pocket-sized bandit in his built-up shoes; I cry on the way to work and over my sodden lunch sandwiches, over my manuscripts and galley proofs. Dancing is no help and Ram's school has gone too.

It is January and Winston Churchill dies. I push my way down to Trafalgar Square through enormous shuffling dark-clad crowds – no-one speaks – and perch on top of an icy-cold bollard. Hours go by with long columns of slow-marching soldiers and airmen and sailors and no-one in the crowd makes a sound. Muffled drums, booming cannons fired thud, thud – at regular intervals. Ranks of bandsmen: funeral marches deep from the heart. Intense paralysing cold.

The columns march past Downing Street, past the grey old mass of the Foreign and Commonwealth Office, the War Office and the Cenotaph. Wartime and blitz and Churchill's growling speeches. Old glory and past British history. Mine, but only by proxy. I sit there, stuck somewhere between cultures. How real in the bone? Long before everyone disperses, I fight my way back though the crowds, on my own, to Clapham.

PART TWO
STREET LIFE

CHAPTER SEVEN
1964

A balloon's got loose and it's floating, high and higher up in the sky until it's just a small black blob above Pembridge Road. I try to follow it as I walk home from Notting Hill Gate Tube and almost fall over the kerb. Somewhere I know there's an unhappy child and a mother saying, "Well, you should have kept a hold of it. I did tell you!"

But I feel just like that balloon.

I feel untethered. I am cut loose from definitions, drifting light as helium: and I have come – wonder of wonders – to rest in Notting Hill (or the Grove, as we locals and savants call it) just where I knew I wanted to be. I knew it the minute I visited a friend of David's with a studio off St Stephens Square. There was something indefinable – undeniable but heady – in the air. It felt and still feels somehow unregulated, open, even ferocious.

Walking home from the Tube every time gives me a thrill. First of all I pass rows of large Victorian houses – pastel-stuccoed and smart – with immaculate front gardens where even the flowering shrubs smell of money. But then, once over Westbourne Grove, it all changes. For a start, there's hardly any traffic. The streets widen and the grand houses are replaced by long terraces all with a shabby bygone elegance. There's no sense of self-regard. The pediments are quietly crumbling, iron balustrades rusting. First-floor windows stretch magisterially from ceiling to floor above unpainted balconies and light pours serenely down the quiet streets. They are becalmed, in a private dream without boundaries that makes me slow down and breathe more deeply.

And then there are the words – here, there and everywhere – scribbled on walls, on phone boxes, shop-fronts, anywhere, with no regard for ownership, property or decorum. Who owns them? I imagine disembodied ghosts racing triumphantly along night time streets. "The Tygers of Wrath are wiser than the Horses of Instruction," they scrawl imperiously. And "Burn it all down!" another instructs. Round the corner in Powis Square and they write, "The road of excess leads to the palace of wisdom."

And here's a longer one:

"Asses, some have litter spread
And with filthy food are spread;
All things have a home but one.
Thou, oh Englishman, hast none."

How energising, how lovely. I have never been anywhere that feels so splendidly restless.

"Notting Hill?" says mother when I phone home to tell them I am moving out of Clapham, "Isn't that where the riots took place?"

"Oh, that was ages ago," I say airily. Well, only five years ago, but I don't mention that.

There are notices pinned up here and there. A local Free School has opened. A protest meeting against the Council is being planned. A Poetry Olympics is being mooted by a poet who lives round the corner from me in Tavistock Square. It is all energy and ferment. For the first time I am in a place where people can come and reinvent themselves, where the population is mixed and history and Empire have been kicked into the long grass. I walk round and round the shabby streets and their closed-off garden squares and what I smell is freedom.

And now, amazingly, I live here: actually live here. Pat has married her architect, Lisa's partner has moved into our old Clapham flat and here I am.

So nearly not. The lettings agent had scores of properties on his books and barely gave me a look. "How much do you earn at your publishing house?" he asks.

"Twelve pounds ten shillings a week."

"The rent's five pounds a week. You can't afford it," he said flatly and turns away. I am dismissed.

I have been too honest I realise. And twelve pounds ten shillings seemed a good wage anyhow. I should have lied. I am no good at lying. But then suddenly I find I am saying in mock Roedeanian, "Actually, my parents give me an allowance."

What rubbish. He'll surely call my bluff...

"Well, in that case..."

... and it works. I sign the contract. I get the keys.

Just two rooms on a corner in a Victorian terrace house. It's up two narrow flights of narrow stairs with rickety banisters, but it is all mine. A shared bathroom is tucked into the turn of the stairs. "Mrs Gordon – Maureen – is an exotic dancer," says the agent's dogsbody rather wistfully as we pass her flat. "And the man on the ground floor writes science fiction." I can glimpse an ancient bath and an even more ancient toilet. A small window doesn't let in much light. Maybe just as well. My two rooms themselves are totally bare – nothing in them except a sink with a cold tap, a square plain wood table and a wobbly kitchen cabinet its owners must have left behind with no regrets.

When Mother comes to inspect, she breathes hard.

"Ach, all that education, and you can't do any better than *this...*"

But I think there is something beautiful about empty space. My two rooms with their simplicity, their handsome dimensions and windows looking down on two streets, fill me with joy.

"And why no bed?" asks Mother. 'Surely you can afford a *bed...*"

I really liked the way my cousins lived in Tilak Road – just unrolling a bed at night-time. So economical, so simple.

"The mattress is fine."

Mother sighs.

"Just because things have always been done one way is no reason..."

"At least I can take you out somewhere decent for lunch? If there's anywhere decent around here..."

It is well over a year since David broke things off and I could have launched a battleship on all my tears. But now it's time to change – unlike the barometer at home – I say resolutely to Lisa.

No more handed-down ideas. No second-hand why should pictures go only on walls? I lay big squares of hardboard on the floor instead of a carpet. In my imagination I thought they would look like gleaming sand. But to be frank, it looks like, well, brown hardboard. I'm going to cover the walls with hessian because I like the texture, but discover I have to size it first with evil-smelling paste and that makes the material go stiff so the sheets are like vast playing cards. I labour manoeuvring them up onto the walls nonetheless. But I don't care, I hum and I work in a blaze of pleasure because as far as the eye can see, through my three big windows facing down two adjacent streets, there are rooftops and possibilities.

The first night on my mattress on the floor, I can hardly settle for excitement. In what feels like first light, I am woken by hoarse cries in the street. An elderly man is leading a horse and cart laden with junk– old sinks, a hip bath, bits of rusty iron – down the road and calling out regularly. Transients, all transients, I am at home. I snuggle back in my mattress and go back to sleep.

At the weekend, I explore my manor. At the very end of the road there's the Rio, a dimly-lit café run by a West Indian, and full of African masks. I buy a paper dress made by a local young designer in a small shop around the corner. Over on Westbourne Grove there's a minimarket with a crate of knobbly green things – 'avocado pears'.

"What do you do with them?"

"Search me, love," says the elderly shop-owner. "Stew them? With custard?"

Someone has painted a large red and yellow dragon, running all the way down the front of their house on Artesian Road next door.

"There must be something in the air," I comment to the young man beside me, as we sit waiting for the machines to stop in the local launderette.

Pushing shoulder-length hair out of his eyes, he agrees.

"Yeah, well, it's the age. It's predicted, astrologically. A time of change. Aquarius rules. Yeah. Just roll with it, man."

We both nod. The machines whine to an end. "A crowd of us," he goes on. "We've got a place on a little island in Spain for the whole summer. It's so cheap! Why not come out?"

He hunts for a scrap of paper in the pockets of his jeans. "Seriously. There's loads of space." He writes his name (Mike) down and the island's name (Formentera). "Come!"

Well... why not?

At 5 a.m. on a summer's Saturday I'm on a sleepy dock waiting for a boat to take me from Ibiza to Formentera. No-one's up but there's a mild sun glinting on the slow swell of the water, and I watch anchored boats swaying and a family of little cats playing around the tables of the quayside cafe. The sun is higher by the time I've found my way over chalky dry paths to Mike's house. It's small, no more than a stone shack, thick-walled and timeless. A small group is sitting out on the grass and there's a guitar and everyone – including the women – is topless. Mike's forgotten he's invited me. Or maybe he just invites everyone he happens to meet. I'm not actually sure he remembers me either. "That's cool," says a German girl. "I've got space, she can stay at mine. I'm Vibeka..."

"Naseem."

"Cool name. Where's it from?"

"India. My father's Indian."

"India, wow, that's so cool. You must know a lot about yoga..."

The island is minute, a tiny lump of rock in the Balearics – nothing here but tranquil peasant smallholdings, a few churches and not a hotel in sight. Crumbly hot earth tracks cut through vineyards and acres of fertile vegetable beds groaning with produce. The dry hot smell of thyme and oregano fills the air. In the heat of the day there is no sound but the high buzz of cicadas that start all together and just as suddenly cut off, as if they've been switched off.

Nobody makes any plans. I have become absorbed into a loose and fluid community, dictated to by the height of the sun. We drift over to spend time with others in their own little houses, or sit outside the Fonda Pepe in San Fernando. Cigarettes from the dim crowded Comestibles are evil black Celtas and cost five pesetas.

"I really should give up," I mutter.

"Yeah," everyone sleepily agrees. In the day we doze, at night it's time for music and togetherness, with spliffs making their way peaceably around. In the softness of the night-time cool, music drifts over the vineyards under high stars. I can hear Daniel who is French and has a sitar, and who likes to play on his own with the door of his little house open. I also know he is not very good, but discard the thought. What is 'good'? People's surnames and stories emerge only in small bursts if ever – different countries they've hailed from, different journeys they've made. Judgements, what do they matter? The whole thing has the pleasant fuzziness of a nice dream.

Two weeks pass somehow. Time to find my suitcase, gather my things and fly back. I have just got through my front door when I can hear my telephone way upstairs. Who can it be? I've had a phone just a few weeks and hardly anyone knows my number. I scramble up the stairs. Keys... where are they? Right at the bottom of my bag with bits of Formentera sand. I burst in and get to the phone. I knock over a vase of dried flowers. Just in time.

"This is The Guardian, the picture desk."

"Who?"

"We wondered if you had any pictures to go with your piece?"

My piece? I've quite forgotten I sent an article in on spec, my very first piece. I never heard so I assumed they didn't like it. And now they're ringing out of the blue wanting *pictures* for it, as if this was the most normal thing and as if I'm a proper writer. There's no way I can pretend this isn't the biggest thing that's ever happened to me.

"You mean you're going to *use it*?"

I could bite my tongue off. I sound so *young*. But he's not really paying attention. I can hear the buzz of a busy office at the other end. For him, this is just routine.

"Well, actually, yes I do have some..."

Afterwards, I sit on the floor surrounded by luggage and dead flowers and scraps of sand. Stunning. Far more stunning than Formentera. Who needs drugs?

I go on taking ideas to the Guardian feeling like a small dog with a hopeful newspaper. And they go on commissioning me. Every time I expect a rejection. I suggest interviewing Martha Graham when she comes to London for the first time with her ground-breaking dance company. "Go ahead," says the Features Editor.

"Yoko Ono?" – "Who? Well, alright... But keep it to eight hundred words." I find myself in a solid mansion block off Regent's Park talking to a slight Ono about the Dance Festival of the Mind she's invented. I sign up for it and receive her instructions with her spidery drawings in the post every day. And to my amazement, Yoko herself writes to me after my piece comes out: 'very intelligently put', she says, 'I hope to see you very soon.' Her writing is as tiny as she is. I interview Pierre Boulez, and then Jane Goodall about taking her infant son, 'Grub', into the jungle to observe gorillas. I hang out at the new Anti-University with David Cooper and R.D.Laing, and I interview Indian musicians. Eventually I decide to take a break and when I get back to go entirely freelance. Even better, Lisa has managed to persuade the agent to let her and Tim rent the little flat directly above mine.

And better still, one day I find a circular from the Asian Music Circle through my door. They are bringing a couple of dance teachers 'of the highest calibre' over from India to teach intensively for two years. At last a class to replace Ram Gopal's vanished ones. Just what I've been waiting for.

But...

"What did you think about Smethwick?" Mother asks on the phone.

"Smethwick?" It seems a long way away from Indian dance.

"That Peter Griffiths getting in – dreadful man. The way he spoke about Asians. Disgusting. The Labour man you know got kicked out, and it was a safe seat!"

Of course I remember but it hadn't seemed that significant – just a by-election. "But it's a fluke, isn't it? All that race talk, it's just National Front stuff, and I remember you said they are just hotheads. There can't be that much support."

"Well," There's a silence. "That's true I said that, now I don't know why but it feels a bit different. But perhaps you're right, I'm making too much of it."

There's a pause while she lights a cigarette. That means Abba must be out. "I don't think the Betta is doing well either. Of course, your father won't admit it, but he's gone all hours trying to drum up orders for the wretched engineering business."

I promise to come home at the weekend.

Abba's still at the surgery when I arrive and when he does get in, he does look tired, to my eyes. His skin has a grey tinge beneath the brown, and that's new. He is abstracted and hardly gives us a glance.

"Here's your coffee," says Mother.

"No time," he says tautly. "I won't have coffee. I've got a meeting at the Pakistani bank."

"Why don't I come with you, Abba? Just for the ride?"

"You must be tired after your journey..." But I can see he's wavering. "It's fine."

"How are things in London?" he asks, as he slowly backs the Jaguar out of the drive. "Are you keeping well? Getting enough rest?"

It's hard to know how to approach him, Abba is always so very guarded and in his present mood, doubly so.

"You were right about the general election," I start off encouragingly, "About Labour getting in."

He shakes his head. "Not good enough – a majority of only four. It makes Wilson very vulnerable. Very vulnerable. It depends what this winter's like. He might need to call another election. Far too shaky position..."

When we arrive at the branch of the Bank of Pakistan, he says, "Come in, they'll like to see you." It's like the days when I was at school and he'd take me in to see patients on his home visits.

"What time's your appointment?"

"No appointment, I don't need an appointment. The manager knows me."

I'm not so sure. I remember the time when he took us to an upmarket Indian restaurant in London. When the waiter politely said that the table he wanted was reserved, he'd said grandly, "Don't you know who I am?" It didn't work then...

But the minute we enter, the clerks come forward en masse. "Doctor Sahib, Mr Mirza will be so pleased to see you. Please come in, take a seat."

I know the drill now. I turn into Pakistani-daughter, and trail behind. And in no time the manager himself emerges from his office.

"Doctor Khan – how you are sitting out here? Come in, come in. You don't need to sit here." He claps his hands and calls a hovering clerk, "What will you take? Tea, coffee?"

When we emerge an hour later, Abba is glowing and the greyness has gone. He walks with his old cocky jauntiness.

"They treat me very well there," he says honestly and hums as he puts the Jaguar into gear. Even his driving now is smoother. "None of this, 'The manager is busy now. Make an appointment...' in English banks. They know how to give respect." He makes a small sound of satisfaction.

"Did you manage to get what you wanted?"

He brushes my question aside.

"Yes, yes. He knows my situation."

"Does the Betta need a loan?"

"Not at all... Maybe for a short while. Business in general is going through a difficult time."

He thinks a bit and then says more seriously.

"I can deal with our own people." He hoots as a lorry tries to overtake. "In the business world there's so much of the old boys' network. It's all Tom, Dickens and Harry." He slows down and peers over the walnut dashboard. Really the Jaguar Mark 4 is too big for him.

"And when I go to meet businessmen, it's always, 'Let's get together and discuss it over a drink'. They meet each other all the time in the pub or at their golf clubs – that's where they do business."

"What do you do?"

"Nothing. When I meet them there I just drink orange juice."

I am what Abba would call getting hot under the collar. I'm sure the men regard him as a wimp. I can just see them sniggering over his head. Boozy bullies. How dare they!

"Still, I'll show them," he goes on. But then, apropos of nothing, "You know what they were shouting at Patrick Gordon Walker – the Labour man who lost in Smethwick – before the election? They were shouting 'Take your niggers away!' And 'If you want a nigger for a neighbour, vote Labour.'"

When Abba takes me to New Street station a few days later to catch my train back to London, he is deliberately jostled by a middle-aged white woman, "Why don't you go back to where you came from?" she shouts. He ignores her but his smile looks fixed. She looked no different from one of his patients.

I remember the warm, safe world of the Pakistani bank later when the new dance sessions start. The teachers that the Asian Music Circle's brought over, Krishna Rao and his wife Chandrabhaga Devi, are gold-star – true dance royalty. They themselves have learned with one of the old ferocious gurus of South India who trace their dance lineage back generations. And they take no hostages with us, expecting far more than Ram ever did. While he taught the basic practice units, *adavus,* Krishna and 'Chandam' have bigger long-term plans. They want a company and by hook or by crook we are going to be it. It's inspiring, their belief, quality and hard work. They're drilling us, day after day – four times a week, in the after-hours staff canteen of the Indian Consulate in Mayfair – till we soak with sweat and exhilaration. We make our way steadily through the long-established traditional repertoire, from 'pure dance' to storytelling items with mime. We tackle dances based on standard *teental,* and then on to more complex rhythms – five beats, seven beats, eleven beats. Krishna throws his head back and roars, "Listen!" throws his pair of sticks that beat time on the ground and storms off. Chandam quietly picks them up and carries on, not missing a beat. We dance on.

The class grows weekly because Indian dance and culture have become visible now. Yoga, world music, the Beatles and their trip to the Maharishi: it has become OK and not a hole-in-the-corner oddity, a little-known and failing class taking place covertly in the backstreets of Chelsea. Indian classical dance seems to be moving towards the mainstream. But not quite…

And then, the day comes when we are allowed to wear ankle-bells and soon after they push us, like little ducklings, on stage. Weekend after weekend, we tour. "Meet us at Marble Arch, at 10am sharp," instructs Krishna and I turn up dutifully with my costume and bells, even though I know our regular minibus won't roll up till way past 11. We racket around the country in it, searching out hired halls, community centres, temples, decommissioned cinemas. We encounter stages where the boards creak when we thump in the way that our South Indian Style – Bharat Natyam – demands, halls where we wait in the wings for hours while worthies make speeches, an old cinema in Southall where tough Sikhs boo and throw stones because they thought we'd be a filmi dance company. None of it ever, ever palls. Dosas, biryani, dhal and laddoos are laid on for us after our performance. "Oh, you like our Indian food," marvel local hosts, because I am pale-skinned. Or they look at my name and think that there must be an Indian husband somewhere. I explain yet again till I am weary that my name is truly my own and that, yes, I do have Indian parentage. It seems that fitting in isn't just a case of fitting in with the English. Everybody, just everybody, thinks in boxes. Why can't I just be who I am?

Punjabi, Gujarati, South Indian events – Independence Days, Republic Days, Diwali celebrations. On the minibus, in different green rooms and in overnight hotels, Krishna and Chandam tell us stories of the way they trained years ago, the struggles, the prejudice against high-caste Indians dancing. "We even cut up her wedding sari to make our costumes!" Krishna exclaims.

We are travelling and being welcomed into a different England existing comfortably undercover. Like the Pakistani bank, it operates in a way that merges old-fashioned Indian respect and courtesy with day to day business. It feels to me like a do-able balance.

CHAPTER EIGHT
1967

It is unbelievable. Worse than a slap in the face. I can hardly bear to listen to the news or open a newspaper, even our own trusted Manchester Guardian. It is as if a dam has burst – everywhere now going on and on about 'immigrants'. The threat they (we?) pose. How many can my homeland Britain take? How can 'the flood' be stopped? Numbers, campaigns, surveys and more numbers. I am living in a country that I do not recognise. The people the papers write about bear no relation to my reality. My cousin Iqbal due to come and take up an engineering job here, my cousin Chand hard at work in south London, the Indian Association, the respectable communities I'd encountered when I was touring with the Indian dance troupe – my own twenty year-old brother who is truly a member of 'the coffee-coloured nation' warned about, even though I myself followed Mother and turned out white. We are caricatured, made unreal and monstrous in all the parliamentary debates around immigration controls. "Fair play," Abba had said confidently about the British. But where is it? Even here in Birmingham, 98% would not let a room to someone 'coloured'. And the Labour Party that we've always supported has broken the promises on immigration they made before the Election. I scrumple the paper up.

"You don't have to go on reading them," points out Moira, my friend from my first job in publishing. "What's the point? You know they're biased." But it's like picking at a scab and being appalled, shaken and angry at what is revealed underneath. Things are not what I thought they were. I have been living under a cosy false premise. I feel as if I have been tossed roughly out of my English cradle. How could I have been so stupid to have believed in it?

A local man writes to the Birmingham Post – the paper we take at home every day with the Manchester Guardian – "*I find myself resenting coloured people driving cars and the bigger the car the bigger the resentment.*" I thought the woman in New Street Station was a one-off, a crazed oddity, Abba'd brushed her aside so firmly. But maybe she wasn't.

Maybe all the people on our local streets as Abba drives around on his doctor's visits are really looking at him in his big Jaguar with undeclared dislike? Too big, too expensive? Was this in Abba's mind when he dreamed up the name 'Julia Masters' for me?

I need to reassess. I am not who I thought I was. I thought I was able to make my own identity. But it is turning out I was wrong. Other people make it for me.

I clump back to my own flat to get back to work. But when I look at the article I've got to finish, I feel even more depressed. I was so proud a few weeks ago when I followed up a story about a woman in deepest suburbia who was famous locally for taking in scores of strays. People said she looked like a shepherd when she took all her dogs out for walks. I'd been curious. What could drive a woman like that? I tracked her down surrounded by thirty or so dogs of all sizes – a tough little woman who'd been in service all her life and used her pension to rescue a first dog who'd been scheduled to be put down. "Human beings are a two-faced lot," she told me bitterly as her dogs – her true best friends – jostled and nosed around her. Back in Ledbury Road, I could still smell dog on my hands as I sat down and started to write my piece.

Looking at it again with the perfidy of Britain overwhelming me, I want to tear it up. Superficial. Idiotic. Irrelevant.

I look outside and Notting Hill doesn't look colourful, free or vivid any longer. How could I have ever been so blind? It's not freedom. It's poor people, crammed into small rooms, intimidated by savage landlords. It's unequal life chances. It's being refused jobs and housing. It's being attacked like Kelso Cochrane was only six years ago right here in Notting Hill. And I am writing about little old ladies and dogs.

"Och no, I wouldn't tear it up," Moira says in her Scottish sensible tones. "It's a nice piece. Just sleep on it."

Mother rings up later that evening. "Why don't you ever come home? You haven't been to see us for months."

"I've been busy."

"Too busy for your family? And don't think I'm going to come and see you in that awful place."

"OK, OK, I'll come home at the weekend. After I've finished the piece I'm writing." I slam the phone down.

The house in Rowlands Road feels oddly quiet when I enter the front door, with that dead feel of an uninhabited house. Bambi looks down at me with his glass eyes and the barometer still registers 'No Change'. Anwar must be in the city centre at college. No-one seems to be around.

But Mother is there. She's in the breakfast room looking out of the window, smoking, and far away. She starts when I come in. "I thought you were going to tell me when you'd arrive..."

"Where's everyone? It's so quiet."

"They're all out. Liesel's in town – you know she's leaving at the end of the month? And Anwar's at college: he's going to be late home."

"And Abba?"

She sniffs. "Your father? Goodness knows. I never see him these days. I think he thinks I run a hotel."

She stubs her cigarette out and immediately picks up her packet of Players again.

"Shouldn't you open the window? Abba's sure to smell cigarettes."

"Let him. Let him try and make a fuss."

"Is he at surgery?"

She gets up and starts towards the kitchen.

"He's never at home. If it's not the Betta... and I wish he'd never started that damn thing, I told him and told him, but he never listens. If it isn't the Betta it's the blasted community." She is filling the kettle. "The community this, the community that, I am sick of the community. They might as well all move in here!"

As if on cue the phone rings.

"You see? It goes on all the time. Wanting advice on immigration, or getting a visa before they bring the new law in, or how to get their family in, or how to get their daughters married..."

"Poor Abba."

"He loves it," she says brusquely. "It makes him feel a big man. All these people coming and buttering him up. All wanting something from him. You're a fool, I tell him. Where will they be when you need them? But he can't see it." She pauses, and adds, "Won't see it."

She sighs suddenly, as if her energy has just drained out of her. It is not like her, this bitterness. Where is my warm-hearted vivid mother?

Birmingham itself I can see has changed. Coming in on the 58 bus from the station, down the Coventry Road through Small Heath and Bordesley Green, I could see the changes. Only a dozen years ago, when Abba and I came accidentally across the first handful of immigrants, they were an unusual sight. I was still at boarding school then and had been fascinated. How different, how exotic they looked, I thought at the time. But Abba didn't. He'd speeded up, I remember, and taken another route. He didn't want to know about the new rural arrivals. And now there's a whole community life on the streets – food shops, travel agents, cinemas.

And families. I realise before I hadn't seen any children, but now there are masses of them. More and more it reminds me of Tilak Road – even the sound of *filmi* music coming from ramshackle garage workshops, even, I could swear, the smell of curry.

"And now there's even talk of building a mosque," says Mother.

"But there is one already."

"Apparently not big enough. He wants something, oh, this big..." she spreads her arms out wide. "Ach, he'll be putting me in purdah next."

It's a ludicrous thought.

"Yeah, I can just see you in a burqah..."

She has the grace to smile. "Let him try."

When Abba comes in much later, he goes straight to his desk in the front room. It is littered with Betta invoices and paperwork and he works steadily there till supper time. I creep in after a few minutes and kiss him silently on his dry cheek; he smiles absently but he doesn't stop. Finally he sweeps the papers aside, takes his glasses off and rubs his eyes,

"If we can just make it to the end of the month..."

Supper is silent. Neither Abba nor Mother meet each others' eyes. A lot of the lasagne is left congealing on the plate.

"I'll need the car tomorrow evening for my ikebana class," she announces as she clears the plates. He doesn't answer. "We're having a special demonstration."

"I need it tomorrow," he says abruptly. She is about to protest but he gets up and leaves the room.

"No, I wasn't surprised," she says tersely as we clear the table together. "Whenever I've got a class, that's what happens. He suddenly discovers that he needs the car. He's against me doing anything that takes me out of the house."

"What about your economics? Weren't you taking O Level ages ago?"

"I didn't take it."

"Why not? You did so much work!"

She fiddles with the washing up liquid and then mumbles, "I made a mistake. I thought the exam was the next day. I arrived too late to take it."

"Oh Mum! What did Abba say? He must have been so..."

"I didn't tell him. Finally, at long last, he got round to asking how it had gone. I told him I'd failed."

"Why on earth?"

"And he *smiled*. I could see he was pleased!"

"Oh no, I can't believe..." But her face has closed up and she already has turned away.

I lie awake a long time. I hear Mother coughing from the bedroom she now occupies. Abba as usual is snoring fit to burst in the master bedroom.

I think about mixed marriages and respect and how Mother's changed. Her lovely resilient buoyancy has gone and their old sparring equality. There's a new bitterness now and a separateness. Has the arrival of co-religionists drawn Abba back to his own roots? Surely he can't want Mother to be like the aunties I'd known in Pakistan, all soft and docile? After all he left his wife behind when he first came to England. Instead he chose Mother with her head-tossing angry western energy.

Being at home in my old bed, I watch the familiar lights of passing cars on the night-time wall as I always did all those years ago. Meanwhile in the outside world, monsters arise – racism, lies and public, bland hypocrisy. I wish I was a child again when things were simple.

"Mrs Laslett makes a difference," people say. "Go and talk to her about the Neighbourhood Service she runs." It's an address just across the road, in Colville Terrace, and The Times agree to commission a small piece. So one rainy morning I decide to do just that. I can hear vague noises as I clatter downstairs in my high-heeled boots. Someone is taking a bath in the vile bathroom. Sooner them than me. And singing too! One of Maureen's men, I bet. She falls in love with a regularity that's touching and that experience never seems to change.

It ought to be springlike outside – after all, it's April – but a sneaky wind's whipping down Artesian Road and rippling the puddles and makes me worried. My Afghan coat smells if it gets damp, and that doesn't seem right for a Times reporter. Maybe it won't have soaked through by the time I get there.

It's so nearby but it feels different. The houses on Colville Terrace are one storey higher than my road and are darker and gloomier. The street itself has a reputation. I go past a house that I've been reliably told is a brothel and another one that hosts late-night blues parties. Both are silent and closed up now – far too early for any action. The houses are run-down and multi-occupied with scores of bells at each front door, and they face an overgrown and locked up garden square. Number 34 looks much the same. Mrs Laslett lives right at the top. I am out of breath by the time I've climbed four storeys, and my coat is definitely giving off the smell of goat.

I knock. No-one comes to the door, but a voice calls, "Come in." Mrs

Laslett is sitting facing me in an old armchair with a blanket over her knees. She looks up enquiringly as I venture in.

"Um, I'm Naseem. We spoke on the phone and you said to come round."

"You are...?"

"Naseem. I rang. I'm a journalist. I'm writing for..."

"Ah yes, The Times. Do you work for the Times?" I don't think she thinks I'm impressive enough. I knew the coat was a mistake.

'Yes, no, well, I'm freelance. I rang you about the Neighbourhood Service"

"I remember. How much do you know about it already? Clear that chair – you can sit over there."

"A bit, but not much. But I do live locally, on Ledbury Road."

She sighs a bit wearily. "How long? I've lived and worked here for over twenty years... Well, ask me your questions."

I get out my pad, and glance at her. She's a spare elderly woman in her fifties, with a drawn high-cheek-boned aquiline face; her hair is greying and pulled tightly back.

"Can you tell me what caused you to start the Neighbourhood Service?" I begin.

"Look around you and I don't think you'd need to ask why." It comes over as sharp and I wince. But then she relents. "It's very easy. It all comes down to housing. All the deprivation and the local need come from that one thing – that's where the basic need is. Most of the houses round here are owned by slum landlords. Often big conglomerates. I can give you all the statistics about overcrowding if you go over to the table over there." She gestures. I realise then that she is disabled.

"The Neighbourhood Service began when I came to know that one of the landlords – a very big company – was secretly in trouble and was probably going to go bankrupt. That rang alarm bells.'

I look enquiring.

"Landlords try everything to get people out of their properties when that happens," she explains. "Empty houses are more valuable than tenanted ones, even when they've got whole families paying rent to be crammed into one room."

"But isn't there legal protection? The Rent Act?" I remember. She nods.

"Indeed. The minute a tenant comes to our Neighbourhood Service to ask for help, we get onto it. We deal with Rent Tribunals, the Council's Public Health Department," she counts them off on one hand, "Housing Officers, Harassment Officers."

I write down the details, and she pauses to give me time to catch up. "We run a legal advice service two nights a week for locals."

"How much does it cost them?"

"Nothing at all. A barrister and a solicitor give their time for free to be on hand." The list goes on of their initiatives – a playgroup, literacy classes for adults, art groups and drama groups, boxing classes for children."

"That's marvellous."

"And now we are looking into forming our own housing association."

This is fight-back in truth. I feel heartened, and on the verge of a new world. The graffiti on the streets never give anything more than just a call to protest. Sometimes they seem to be simply puerile pure theatre. Someone, I see, has even jokily altered 'The road of excess leads to temple of Wisdom' to 'temple of Willesden'. But here...

"And a forum of residents has come together."

Finally, she pauses. She seems tired and I want to go away and digest. "I think I've given you enough, don't you think?"

I nod. I have pages of notes.

"Call me if you have any queries."

I'm just packing up when there's a knock at Mrs Laslett's door and before she can say anything, a young black man has come bounding in, shaking off spots of rain like a happy Labrador. The atmosphere instantly changes.

'Courtney...' says Mrs Laslett warmly, putting her hand out as he crosses the room. "Do come in. Miss Khan is just leaving."

'You're a journalist?' he says. My shorthand pad is a giveaway of course. He pulls out a chair and perches on its edge as if he had too much energy to sit back fully. "Freelance?"

"Yes. I live around the corner."

"We've just finished our interview. This is Courtney," Mrs Laslett explains.

"Did she tell you about our plans for Carnival?" he asks.

I shake my head. Yet another thing Mrs Laslett's organising, and we never even touched that.

"Give me your phone number. We can talk. I'll get in touch if I hear of any good stories. We writers, we need to stick together."

Is this a pick-up line? I wonder, as I squelch back over to Ledbury Road. I rather hope so. He's like an electric light. He lights the room up. And lovely almond-shaped eyes. I hope he rings.

I sit down to write it. It's an impressive story – very sobering, very solid. And in a different world from a piece about dogs. I shouldn't dress

85

it up, I tell myself firmly. Let it tell itself. I file my copy, being careful to leave out any mention of Mrs Laslett's disability. It would be demeaning to present her as an invalid. I had carefully not asked her about it. I may be young on the block but at least I know that.

A week later, the piece appears. I'm not sure about the title "Notting Hill Rises Up" but that's down to the subs and otherwise it reads well. But then I get to the end, and I sit up sharply.

My phone rings an hour later. Courtney. "So, have they used your piece?"

"Yes... but you know what?" I am incensed, "They changed it!"

"What do you mean?"

"Just listen to this, it's the last bit, 'Mrs Laslett suffers from Multiple Sclerosis. She runs the service from her bed, with no secretary and a constant shortage of money."

"So..?"

"I never wrote that! And she wasn't in bed either. I rang and complained and you know what... they said Mrs Laslett herself rang up! She asked if I'd mentioned she's disabled in my article!'

He's got to agree. We all know a journo's copy is sacred. But instead, he laughs!

"Of course she rang them! What did you expect?"

"And she dictated that sentence herself, the guy at the Times said!"

He clicks his tongue, "She's quite a piece of work." It sounds very like admiration.

"Yes, but it's my copy..." But I know I am whining now.

"Oh, come on, lighten up! It's not so bad. So tell me, what else are you up to?"

And we talk on for nearly an hour, about housing and migration and the Grove and the shabbiness of government and the White Paper until my hand holding the phone starts to ache and I need to go downstairs to the horrible toilet to pee.

Then the next day there's a ring on my bell, and Courtney comes in as if he owns the place. He drops his leather coat on the floor, prowls around and pokes around my cupboards to see what there is to eat.

"Where's the coffee?' And that becomes the pattern of the days.

"Y'know, it's amazing I've never come across him before," I muse to Moira who's taking the flat upstairs now Lisa and Tim have moved. "Now I see him everywhere I go. He was at the People's Centre the other day, and at the youth centre meeting about police harassment, and I'm sure I saw him at Release."

"Maybe you just never noticed him before?"

"Unlikely, he's pretty noticeable, you must agree – all that eloquence and energy. He comes into a room and it lights up."

"Mmm," is all she says.

"He's so *alive*."

"He's certainly very charming," She makes it sounds like an insult, "But what do you know about him? Where does he live, for instance? How does he earn his living?"

"Oh, you – you sound just like my mother."

Well, Courtney might be light on facts, but there's something about him – a core of independence that makes sense to me, as if he doesn't want to fit into any one world entirely.

Walking down Ledbury Road with him is slow because one after another person we pass will stop and accost him and high-fives him or simply shout, "Hey man..!" It's like a cross-section of Grove residents – hippies in floppy tie-dyed gear, the local community-minded Methodist minister, cool dudes who mutter enigmatically behind black shades. Who does Courtney not know or make his number with? It's so extreme that I start laughing.

"What's up?" he sounds nettled.

"Nothing. It's just that you know everybody. Who was that just now?"

"That? That was Hoppy, you've got to know him – John Hopkins. He's started International Times. The chick with him? That was Suzy Creamcheese."

"See what I mean, all these local icons? Then there was the guy from Pink Floyd, and the Mangrove..."

He looks pleased and hums, "Like fish in water, man. Move with it."

"And I bet you were at the Poetry Olympics, and the Dialectics of Liberation too?"

"What's this? Checking up on me?"

"No. I was there too."

"Of course you were," and he hugs me. Courtney's hugs could break your bones.

We come to the corner of Acklam Road where a small black boy is handing out leaflets. A meeting to protest about Sergeant Pulley at Notting Dale police station who is notorious for racist savagery in the area.

He takes one courteously and stands reading it. "Thanks, little brother." The child tries to look serious, but beams: big white smile in his little face.

"You know," says Moira approvingly when we both share a Nescafe break, "He's got his head screwed on the right way. He's not like all those activists who know their Marx and come here to lead the masses."

"Ah, now you get him."

"I take my time."

He does charm, Courtney. And he has charmed Moira who has no time for people she considers champagne socialists.

There's protest everywhere these days in the Grove and it feels good. I spend my evenings in meetings about Rent Tribunals and housing plans. Mrs Laslett was right, slum landlords are rife – there's a block in Colville Gardens where the flats have been sub-divided into smaller and smaller rooms with a whole family in each. Maybe I can place a story somewhere about it. I drop by the People's Centre to pick up leaflets.

"The guy in the basement of one of those houses," the student volunteer points out, "Doesn't even have electricity. He has to use candles. And the walls of the place are just running with damp."

"Can't he to go the Rent Tribunal?"

"Of course he should. But we know tenants who've tried that and were given notice to quit. Or their landlords let rooms in the same house to prostitutes. And if that doesn't work, they visit with big dogs or ring their door bell incessantly late at night, especially if people have children."

I go over the figures again when I get home. "Two hundred and ten people squashed into just nine houses, and seventy-two children under the age of ten," I read aloud to Courtney. "Shameful."

He shrugs. So what's new? He knows all this already but I am learning all the time. We are sprawled across my mattress, and while Courtney is deep in another section of the newspaper (probably the Sport, I suspect) and I am reading about pudgy Edward Heath talking to Tory women about race relations. Control numbers, he says, encourage people to return, go back to where they came from.

Discrimination, prejudice, racism and all backed up with such clear evidence. I shake my head over the big new Policy and Economic Planning report. So clear, so conclusive. In every nine cases of out ten they looked at, claims of discrimination were proved.

I get my pencil out and mark story after story, looking for the human dimension. There are real people behind the neutral figures. 'Application to foundry for vacancy as a labourer, was told: "No vacancy and why don't you go back to your own country."'

I think of Abba and the woman on the railway station,

"Applied to a public office for a job. I was given a job behind the scenes and not allowed to mix with the public. It was said in my presence that the public did not like coloured people. So I was not given a clerical officer's job although I am a graduate and better educated than my superiors."

I think of Abba not being able to make it as a surgeon because of his colour. Or make it as a businessman.

So much to do, but at least here in the Grove we are fighting and I feel safe in company.

It's late at night, I wonder what Courtney is up to. He was talking about going up to the new Black House that Michael de Freitas has started, wherever that is. I don't like to probe or be nosy. There are times when I don't know what he is thinking, when he sinks into gloom, and he won't speak and takes offence at things that were not meant as criticisms. At times he vanishes for days. I do not tell Moira.

But a few days later he is back, confident and bouncy. And one day, he is pacing up and down my front room when he says reflectively,

"You know what we need in the Grove?"

"Mmm?" I say. I'm trying to put a new ribbon into my typewriter and getting ink smudges everywhere.

"What we need is a newspaper," he says thoughtfully.

Well, I can think of many things the Grove needs – an end to rapacious landlords, a curb on racist police, green space for children to play in... But a newspaper??

"You can't be serious?"

"Think of it – all the stories we could run that editors would never touch. We'd be speaking from the streets, man, from the things we know, things everyone knows and the mainstream press won't touch." He comes and sits down beside me and hits the table with his hand, "A real community newspaper. Out of our own community. Think of the power. Think of it!"

"Think of the work. Think of the cost. Think of how to do it!"

"Don't worry. I'll set it up. I'll do it all." He gets up abruptly and starts to lace up his trainers. "I'm splitting," he says.

"Are you coming back?"

"Can't say." His mind is clearly somewhere else. "Got to move – catch you later..."

And early one Saturday evening, there's a clattering and there's Courtney shepherding a group of people – some of whom I recognise from the street – up my narrow stairs. "Told you so!" says his tacit and clearly smug look. These are the people he has gathered – true to his word – all of whom want to be part of a community newspaper. They pack my front room, around a dozen or so, sprawling over the mattress

89

and floor cushions as I urgently hunt for mugs and glasses. There's a loud hum of conversation and an air of great anticipation. Something is happening. The feeling is palpable. We have all been fired by Courtney whose special talent is the ability to fire people up.

We are so different – does it matter? I recognise a willowy American trustafarian who's doing her Master's in the Grove, a black radical poet and a small fierce Maoist woman with the chubby face of a pretty child. Courtney proudly introduces Raju, a shy Indian student. "He's studying law and that'll be useful, man!" And Gunther, a German left-wing photographer, and his artist wife are already old friends. We all see a different newspaper. By force of habit, I scribble down the ideas and page follows page. A black revolutionary tract, a Digger-like free-sheet, a base for new writing ("Yes!" I think privately), a grassroots New Society – we want all of them. We want to cover the University of the Streets and the anti-Vietnam demos, local police harassment, the push for a community fund, the absence of day nurseries... ("Day nurseries!" exclaims the Maoist, disgusted by the timidity of the ideas. "It's time we started a revolution!" and seems about to storm out.) Well, why not all? Even the differences are intoxicating, and show the wide spectrum of things we want to change. The possibilities are endless, the need is endless. A voice for the Grove? Of course.

"What about design?" asks the poet. "It's got to look cool."

"She can do it," says Courtney, pointing to me. "She's been to printing school." I start to protest, but it's no use and no-one questions my skills. Gunther says he will contribute photographs. The poet will look after the literary side. Courtney offers a column. The American will monitor and report on the Council's decisions.

A crossword, someone proposes. Horoscopes. "Superstition," objects the poet, but he is shouted down.

"But where will the money come from?" asks the quiet Indian in a pause. He's an unlikely candidate for a radical newspaper – sedate and modest and conservative in manner. But he's right in this. Where *is* the money going to come from?

"Easy," says the American confidently. "From advertisers. We'll sell copy."

"But no-one here has any money."

"Wrong. There's local businesses – places like Roy's Gym and the Safari Tent – and there's publishers, plus people who'd be glad to support a local venture..."

"How much will it cost?" persists the law student.

Courtney looks at me. I seem to have become the expert. "Well, we'll need to decide on a format," I say slowly, reaching back to my evening classes in graphic design. "And then I can do a word count..." It sounds convincing, but it feels more like assembling a newspaper from DIY instructions.

And then there's the matter of a title...

"Hard Times."

"News from the Grove."

"Tell It Like it is."

"The Ghetto Gazette"

"'Street Talk – Straight Talk."

Are we going to be here all night, I think, as people yell different suggestions. Will I ever be able to clear them off my mattress and go to bed?

"The Hustler," cuts in Courtney. "That's it!" and, firmly, "That's what it's got to be."

He's right. It's sassy, it's bold. It's in your face.

We've got a title. We've got enough ideas for six hundred newspapers. We all decide that we are a collective. We all know that hierarchies are an establishment power game – definitely no editor.

We divide up jobs and set ourselves deadlines. People are detailed to approach local businesses and get them to advertise. Now it's over to me.

I have never designed a paper in my life. But come down to it, who's done any of this before? They all finally go away with a lot of noise and laughter on the stairs, leaving overflowing ashtrays and dirty mugs and glasses. I am too tired to do anything about any of it.

But it strikes me as I sit up in bed thinking about type-faces, column inches, and paper sizes that something has quietly changed. I have always thought I was a commentator on the sidelines but it seems I am an actor. It is a new thought. I turn it over in my mind with a sense of both doubt and wonder. If I wasn't so anxious, I'd laugh with amazement.

CHAPTER NINE
1968

OK, this is it. I'm all ready for it. Bring it on.

I've gone back to the lessons learned in evenings spent tracing letters, word counts and casting off copy. I've unearthed my big book of typefaces, scalpel and T-square. And now I'm sitting, waiting. I feel like a surgeon whose instruments are all laid out at the ready. Now all I need is the body...

And here come the articles. They drop through my letterbox in dribs and drabs stealthily in the night. A few – like American Vanessa's – are carefully typed, but an awful lot arrive on lined pages torn out of exercise books. And all my careful stipulations about length, I might as well have saved my breath. I unzip the case of my little grey portable and take out sheets of carbon paper. The heap grows steadily. There's an awful lot. But there's a rough urgency about it that's exciting while scaring me too.

"Here's some more," says Courtney, fishing them crumpled out of his duffel coat pockets and puts them on my kitchen table. A piece on rent control, and a long poem by Foster the poet that goes over three pages. I am not sure if I am strong enough to tackle him. "Can't you speak to him?" but Courtney is not listening.

"We can't use all this." I protest. There are news stories and book reviews and pieces that Courtney's been given by the Anti-Vietnam protestors, and arts of course, plus a strip-cartoon and even horoscopes despite the ideological objections.

Courtney doesn't see any problem. He puts a copy of the underground International Times down. "IT does it," he says and turns over its pages where they're knocking the secretive Bilderberg conference and next to it announcing a so-called Hip Trip – a boat chartered to bring seven hundred West Coast hippies to Britain. ("They'll certainly end up in the Grove if that ever happens," I say acidly). IT's pages are just as eclectic, and maybe eclectic is political too.

And Courtney is right, we do aim to be inclusive. We do want to reflect our area and, OK, to break the mould. "If you want to understand a community," he always says, "You have to make a map." So maybe the *Hustler*'s not so much a newspaper as a map. Black, white, arts, revolution, reform. Race does not matter: action does.

I type and tidy till my fingers are numb and mark it all up as I was taught. And finally off it all goes to the typesetter.

And it comes back, transformed. All these oddments of higgledy pieces have turned into neat long rivers of shiny type. Strips and strips of them tumble out of the large brown envelope. It is a miracle. Chaos has been magicked into order.

I'd like to sit and gloat over it for ever, stroking the smooth pristine strips, and even Courtney is silent. But I have to chop it all up. It feels like cutting up a first-born. But it has to be done.

I pick up the first sheet. "Pass me the scalpel..." I know my hand will tremble, and it does. I press too hard and there are scratch marks on the table when I lift the strip up. I swallow hard and carry on. Snip, go the columns of type and the margins whisper softly to the floor that's slowly filling with debris.

Courtney peers over my shoulder, and others from the team drop by to watch, but it is not a spectator sport, and gradually they all drift off. "Come and join us in the pub," they call, but I know I won't. I am pleased they've gone. The day is drawing in. I draw the hessian curtains and shut out the Grove. I light another cigarette and look at the boards with their pencilled outlines of pages and columns. Then I look at the heaps and heaps of strips of words. Here's the thing – how to fit them all in?

Start at the front page and the jagged form of our logo, an exploding '*Hustler!*' And then simply pictures, we'd decided, and all the wildly contradictory quotes about our area that please us so much. "A social dustbin," said The Times. We are 'a transit area of vagrants, gypsies and casual workers' for a social science text book. 'A square mile of squalor' and 'a nice homey area, but needs cleaning up," said a local. And a little girl says crossly, 'It's fine but the roads are too bumpy to roller-skate.'

I pause for a cigarette and a cup of coffee. The ads look good and they'll pay for the printing costs. Injun Dog on Portobello Road wants to push their 'Kinky sun glasses' (7/6). Frank Critchelow, who owns the Rio at the end of my road, is starting a Safari Tent for "Turn-on West Indian feasts!" And Roy's Gym that rings with the sounds of thumps and hollers when I pass it, is here too. And now for the articles...

Hours go by and when I'm done, the floor is thick with scraps of paper, and my hands are sticky and I can hardly breathe for the acrid smell of Cow-Gum. But it's there, our first laid-out eight-page *Hustler* firmly down on four big boards. It's too late to call Courtney and who knows where he is – or who he is with – anyhow. I prowl around my two rooms feeling too tired and too wired to go to bed.

All the team is here when packets of the finished *Hustler* come back, but there's no time to stop and admire them. The People's Association have called a big meeting in All Saints Hall about the crisis in local housing. Mrs Laslett was right – it is a scandal. Courtney tucks a pile of new *Hustlers* under his arm and is gone. "Catch me up..."

The hall's already crowded when we get there, rows and rows of metal chairs, and I find myself stuck somewhere near the back. Where's Courtney? Oh there, right at the front near the stage, deep in conversation with Hoppy of IT fame. We seed ourselves wherever we can here and there among the throng. It's such a mix – street activists and squatters, tenants, politicians and community workers. We've got here just as half a dozen people are starting to make their way up onto the rostrum and the noise hushes. I know most of them already now – George Clark of the People's Association who's an old hand, Bruce Douglas-Mann our MP, Donald Chesworth from the Methodists. There's someone from the tenants' association and the Free School, but not Mrs Laslett. I think I can see Michael X surrounded by a small group from RAAS – the rude acronym for his Racial Adjustment Awareness Society – to one side.

Meetings get called many times round here, but this one's charged. There is real anger and alarm. The word is out that the company owning the big row of houses in Colville Terrace is in trouble and is planning to sell up. We live in a feral state where greed wins hands down. And Colville Terrace is just the start of it – as many as 834 families in Golborne Ward alone, one speaker adds, need rehousing. An officer from Kensington Council tries statistics: "Rehousing would cost your Council £3,500 for every family. It would mean putting up the rates for everyone." It cuts no ice. He tries to come back. "Putting up the rates is one of the hardest political nuts to crack." Not our problem. No sympathy here.

The audience is vocal and I scribble things down for *Hustler 2* as people shout from the body of the hall.

"It's not all the Council's fault," one woman calls out. "People just don't use the existing services enough. They should go to the Housing Department and get on the list."

"The Council? What have they ever done for North Kensington?"

"UDI for North Kensington!" shouts someone, maybe not entirely in jest. A headline? I scribble it down. Control is the issue. Absentee landlords, distant Council. No rights. No voice.

George Clark, who is a local heavyweight, struggles to make himself heard over the general melee.

"We should set up some kind of across-the-board community fund – a Community Action Fund," he argues, "Take control for ourselves." But none of the tenants' associations present or other local action groups want to join his working group. He sits down and shakes his head decisively. "I'm not prepared to go it alone," he says. "That wouldn't be good for me, and it wouldn't be good for Notting Hill."

People now have the bit fully between their teeth and the list of angry grievances grows. Housing, police harassment, extortion, absence of play space, Barclays Bank's South African connections ("Start our own banks!"), the list goes on and it is not clear how the organisers will be able to channel the issues into action. It cannot go on like this. We split again into smaller groups and smaller actions, united only by a sense that something has to change. At the end, we burst out of the hall into the dark of All Saints Road. Our copies of the *Hustler* go rapidly – "Just a shilling!" At this rate, we'll have to increase the print run. And we have our lead for issue two.

And in no time we need to get *Hustler* 2 together. There's no problem about material. Whatever we lack in the Grove, it's not stories. But where's the money?

"But we got advertisements," says Vanessa. "So, where's the problem?"

Raju, who collected the ads and is a gentle upright character, riffles his papers and looks troubled. He mumbles, "Yes, it's true. We should be able to cover our costs from advertising and sales. It costs us seventy pounds to print a thousand copies, and we raised a hundred and twenty."

"Then?"

"But on paper."

We look at his paperwork. Publishers have paid promptly for their ads, but community advertisers have not.

"What about this bill for Roy's Gym," Vanessa immediately notices. "They can pay."

Raju looks even unhappier. "When they know it's me, they won't come to the phone."

"Go and visit them in person. Don't go away."

"Oh, I'm not sure they'd like that..."

"For crying out loud!"

It is tenuous, but we manage: we send out SOSs and we carry on. And so do the stories.

We are at the axis of action, here in the Grove and internationally.

America's Black Panthers are local heroes. Their pictures – so super cool in black leather jackets, military berets and those impenetrable black shades – are stuck up in local shops and cafes. And the sisters, imposing with their vast soft Afros and African dashikis. We cover struggles in the States, and James Baldwin's new book. Eddie Braithwaite lets us run his new Caribbean saga-poem all over the central spread. We run between Black Book Fairs and underground events, meetings and demos. This is what belonging means, I think as I tear off downstairs to yet another attempt to nail Kensington & Chelsea District Council.

When the 1968 Mexican Olympics take place and John Carlos and Tommie Smith raise their arms in a Black Power salute, we immediately run it all over the front page. The issue is hardly off the press before it's snatched up. We increase the print order. A fan from Holland sends a cutting from a Dutch paper: 'If you want to know what's happening in Britain, read the *Hustler*.' And the Observer notes: 'There's a new fortnightly paper being sold for one shilling around Notting Hill in London, which just might turn into something really good.' They send a female journalist and a photographer round to Ledbury Road.

I groan when I read their published piece – I am described as 'gentle and serious'. "That means boring," I complain.

But Courtney is 'electrically noisy, disconcerting and talks the rude, vivid language of Black Power...' In the picture between us, Darcus Howe – a member of Michael X's group – is looking understandably quizzical.

I am trying to sort out the contents for Issue 3 when my door-bell rings many times and someone bangs on the front door.

"Come down quickly," shouts Raju. "They're storming Powis Square!"

I grab my bag and run. I can hear a low growl and drumming coming from a few streets away, getting louder and louder as we race over Ledbury Road and along Colville Terrace.

The square is full of a very large crowd of local people all massing along the mesh fence. They're launching themselves at it, time and again, all together, in waves.

"Down! Down!"

"And again!"

There's a roar and then wild cheers as the chain link fence starts to quiver. But it doesn't give.

"Again!"

I am caught up in the crowd and try and push through to get a better view. "Where's Gunther?" I shout to Raju. "We've *got* to have pictures of this!" And there our photographer is, clicking crisply away. He gives a laconic thumbs up and leaps up onto a rubbish bin to get overhead shots.

It takes time and we have to charge again and again but finally the fence buckles and gives and we all pour jubilantly, cheering, into the overgrown neglected space, all weeds and empty bottles. And there's a sudden pause. What do we do now? Shouldn't someone tell us? But the feeling passes and soon people are posing for pictures, lighting up cigarettes and talking about what can be done for children in the space – till now scandalously the realm of private landlords. And now liberated. A child is knocked over every five days here, says a woman from the newly-formed Play Association, because there's been nowhere else but the street for them to play. She looks happily over the space in all its dereliction. Easy, they can dig out the nettles and can landscape it. Power to the people.

We start to trickle away back to our various flats and homes, flushed with victory, and the sense that at last something positive has been done. We have taken our lives into our own hands

A few days later and the fence has been put back up again by the landlords. We take it down again.

A playground is not a revolution, but it is better than nothing.

Small victories are needed because at times it is hard to keep my spirits up. Something is changing and I don't quite know what. There was such a united camaraderie in the *Hustler's* early days and it seems to have evaporated. Courtney and I are not getting on well either. He is short and evasive and takes me up over details. Is it race? If I was black instead of half one thing and half another, might things be different? But we never based things on race alone.

Then, before Issue 4, Courtney vanishes and I hear nothing from him.

"I think he said something about going to Nottingham," Vanessa reports vaguely. "Or was it Brighton...?"

And he's still not here when the phone rings. It's Abba calling, from home. My heart sinks – more pressure, I suppose, to move and to buy my own place. I am not wrong it is not a social call.

"Ah, I'm glad I've found you." His voice sounds tired and strained. "I've some sad news to tell you. Your sister Shamim, has died."

Will I go to her flat, he asks.

"It'll need packing up. Her landlady wants to let the place." Of course I agree. He has to give me the address. I've not made contact with her, not for years, our lives diverged so much. And I have never been able to lose a feeling of sadness and failure where Shamim is concerned.

It's a small place, just a bedsitter and a kitchenette, in neutral Earl's Court. It is untidy. Shamim's clothes are still strewn here and there and the bed is unmade. It does not smell fresh. "Gundi bu," Abba would sniff. I hesitate on the threshold. I do not want to be here. It feels like an intrusion. A pale green Benarsi sari lies crumpled on the floor inside the flimsy dark wood wardrobe. I recognise it. Abba and I brought it back for Shamim when we were in Pakistan for Nafees and Maqbool's wedding. "It's too pale for my complexion," she had said. "I'm too dark." Beside the sari there's a plastic bag. Inside are two aubergines and six onions.

"Why was she on her own?" I ask Abba when I ring him back. "I thought she got married?"

He makes a sound of disgust. "He was no good. Crazy fellow."

"Shouldn't we tell him?"

"No, leave him out of it."

I meet Abba at the undertaker's in Whitechapel. It is January and very cold and the hearse is not there. "Come in, come up and have a cup of tea," invites the imam's wife, a large chatty East End woman. We follow her up narrow stairs into their little sitting room. It overlooks the main arterial road, is crammed and over-heated, and full of the twitter of caged birds. Abba and I sit there uneasily as Mrs Ali bustles round with tea-cups, breaking off from time to time to address the birds in baby language, and talk about death. "Beautiful, she looked," she tells us, "I washed your daughter and anointed her myself, just as our religion requires. You will want to see her, of course."

"Er... yes."

We are led downstairs again and into a small chilly building and there she is, lying in her coffin. She is without her glasses and looks young, her face round and chubby with no lines. And peaceful. I don't know how to take all this – the chat and the tea-cups and the imam himself who is a brisk skinny old man with a thin white beard, and almost skittish. I've never been to a funeral before, let alone a Muslim one, but shouldn't he be treating it with more gravity?

"Ah, here's the hearse. Time to go." The imam looks at his watch and signs to his men to close the coffin, and then he stops them. "No, wait. She's still got her rings on." He bends over the coffin and pulls them off abruptly one by one and hands them to Abba who looks at them as if he doesn't know what to do with them. Somehow this seems the most shocking thing of all.

We sit without speaking in the funeral car that follows the hearse as it weaves and bounces its erratic way through London traffic that pays it little attention. Sometimes the hearse goes so fast that our car has problems finding it and catching up. I hold onto the side as we swerve this way and that. So casual, as if we were disposing Shamim like a lot of recycling. Where's the dignity? Where's the sense of significance? The coffin at the back of the speeding hearse when we catch sight of it in a gap between lorries looks extremely small.

I'm exhausted when I get back home and Abba has left to go back to Birmingham. There's still no sign of Courtney. Raju rings up to see how I am. "You need light relief. Come to the cinema." The cinema in Queensway is showing 'Carry on Up the Khyber'. High jinks in pseudo-harems, Kenneth Williams posing and posturing as a lascivious sultan. Lots of jokes about underpants. It is wonderfully innocent. But a sad and bewildering world.

When Michael X – elevated now from his original 'Michael de Freitas' comes to visit, I open the front door and take a step back. He's the last person I expected. I didn't think he even knew where I lived. I lead the way upstairs feeling nervous, as if royalty has come to visit. No coffee, he says firmly: he doesn't believe in polluting the body. We settle for herbal tea. I make rather uneasy conversation and skirt around anything heavy and I am constantly uncertain why he has come. I have a sense of being looked over. I know it is not sex. He's not an attractive man. His skin is flabby and slightly yellow in tone, and I think of Courtney's lovely burnished blackness and his simple clean feeling of existing without a history.

Talk turns to *The Hustler* and I wonder if he maybe wants to challenge its stance or its politics. It must seem soft-edged to him. But we don't get into politics either and I'm puzzled where this is going. I mention money and the struggle to keep the paper going.

"Ah, when I was in Reading," he says, and settles back in my cane chair, resting both hands now on the top of the carved ceremonial African-style walking stick he carries. "There was this elderly Jamaican woman whose husband had died, and I knew he left her loaded. She wanted me to go to visit her husband's grave with her to pray so we went there together one evening. Now, without her knowing, I slipped her a tab of LSD. Well, in no time she was seeing such visions!'" He tossed his head back and laughed. "She was so sure her husband was present and was talking to her. And she became totally convinced that I must be a really great shaman. After that," he laughs, "I had no problems at all in asking for bread. None at all."

What am I meant to make of this – an example of his cleverness? But then I get it. I'm not meant to make anything at all of it, I was being assessed and he has judged me to be harmless. My opinion does not matter.

And then finally Courtney does come back and it's all as it was before. He seems to know about the visit. Or almost. "Michael said he'd put you straight about the paper..."

"Oh, really...?"

He carries on regardless.

"He said you were worried about being half white."

"What do you mean? It never came up. I asked him about his own parentage, and how difficult that had been. That's all."

I catch the smell of malice – duplicity, and not casual gossip – behind my back, and I don't like it. Who is being straight? Who is using whom? I feel unsafe. I am weary of the suspicion and the paranoia and the anti-whiteness and I'm tired of living in a half world of angry shadows.

Then this guy Marvin starts to visit. He takes a caustic pleasure out of the change in the air and approves, I think. He sits back in the rocking chair I'd bought in one of the local junk shops that crowd the Grove.

"There's only one way to make a difference," he says. "You know how I stopped things when there was all that rioting in '58?"

"When Kelso was killed?"

"And the police, they just stood back and let the youth smash up the Grove. What did they care? So I took some of the brothers and we drove down to Kensington to one of those nice streets where there was a crowd of white people waiting for a bus. And we stopped and got out, and we beat them up, man. Beat them up nice! After that the police came into the Grove pretty smartly and stopped the violence."

Who can believe anyone? Or know for sure what anyone's agenda really is? Courtney talks about Special Branch spies in the Grove, and so do others. I am picking my way blindfold through not so much a maze as a minefield. Even my own street – just where I thought I was safe, on my own doorstep – delivers evil.

We're coming home from a trip to the printer – Raju, Courtney and me – a few days later. We are relieved and jubilant. We've put another issue successfully to bed in the hands of our taciturn printer. It's turned out fine. We're nearly home and Ledbury Road is opening its arms welcomingly. The sky has been washed clean of rain and everything feels spacious. It's a weekday and people generally are at work. There are just two guys coming towards us from Artesian Road.

"And here we are, doing bugger all," grins Courtney with a cheerful gesture of one arm.

We don't really pay attention to the men, short-haired, tough-looking men in their mid-thirties, who are drawing near. They stop and turn round, both together. In unison.

"You mean us?"

"Us, doing fuck all?"

The morning goes quiet.

"No bro, no," says Courtney cheerfully...

"Yes, we heard you. Don't think you can get out of it."

"Police!" they say and whip out badges. In a parody of cops and robbers; in a studied casual way. But they are not actors. We freeze. We don't know how to deal with this. Even Courtney – ebullient Courtney – is silenced. Who are we are, what are we doing, where are we going – they shoot questions at us. And I feel in the wrong, though I know I am not. They play with us for a while just so we know they are in charge. It is casual and brutal. Then they let us go.

We are outside my house and scuttle upstairs as fast as we can and shut the door. We don't want to look at each other. Every shred of achievement has gone. Though there is no reason for it, somehow we feel ashamed.

Then Marvin stops coming by for no reason. It is as if a shadow has settled, and that's not because of the season. Some of our young paper boys who sell the *Hustler* on the street also give up.

"Maybe because it is getting into autumn," I say to Vanessa uneasily, "And they don't like to be out when it's dark."

We both know this is not the case. But she's due to return to the States soon and says she's got to pull back. Raju's exams are approaching and he's got to shut himself up with his books.

And then the word comes down from the Black House that Michael and his Black Eagles are not happy with the *Hustler* and its coverage. It needs to be a black paper, they say. Enough of housing issues and all that white bourgeois crap.

"And if it isn't?" I say bravely.

"We can stop it," they say.

"They can, you know," warns Raju soberly. "You know, Naseem," he says out of the blue, "You should get married."

Married? To whom?

And he leaves.

It's a bad night on my mattress. I sleep badly. Moira upstairs is away, Courtney is on one of his periodic vanishes and there is no-one to talk to.

I've got deadlines but can't get down to them. And I am out of cigarettes too.

The next day an invitation arrives – a conference about Caribbean arts, out of London, in a university. Even better, it's from CAM, the respected Caribbean Artists' Movement set up by a number of weighty older writers and artists, a very different scene from my local radicals. Three days in the country away from the Grove and into the pure air of sheer reason... So I pack a small bag and set off for Canterbury. I can write a piece too for the next *Hustler*, so I am not running away – honest. Cool straightforward arguments, rationality, absence of anger and passion: I do so need them.

The conference centre is crowded. The hall and the side rooms and even the corridors are noisy with introductions and conversation. Everyone is here – the respected seniors of our own black arts movement, substantial figures, artists and thinkers – Andrew Salkey, John La Rose, Eddie Braithwaite, Aubrey Williams and even mighty Wilson Harris is due. People have come from all over – the Caribbean, Europe, South Africa – to debate West Indian arts.

But if I have come for cool arguments, I have come to the wrong place. A contingent has come straight from a debate on Black Power at London's West Indian Students Centre and they pull the conference away from Caribbean arts back to politics and racism in Britain. They are rude, cutting and ruthless. They pull icons off their pedestals – there go Naipaul and Edgar Mittelholzer and his 'racially bigoted melodramas'. And they tear into the basis for this conference itself. I hunch back in my chair as the arguments and accusations rage. Why are we meeting here? Why are we not in Brixton? "You haven't heard a damn thing we've been doing!" a CAM committee member shouts back. Tempers rise, fray, agendas are jettisoned, integrity is questioned.

I am being thrust right back to *Hustler's* issues and our attempts to preserve a broad view. Through the modern plate glass windows far below stretches the misty view of Canterbury, a safe distance far from the hoi-polloi. Battle rages between the older writers and the street Marxists. I veer between one and the other, moved – as who could not be? – by the clarion call to duty and to arms. What is the artist's responsibility – and above all, the black artist's? The challenge rips passionately through every session – analyses of novels, the state of West Indian culture, African roots. The critics will not let it go and shake the conference. Artistic freedom? They scoff. How can an artist be free when his own people are in chains? Until we can really make our art functional and collective and committed we are not artists at all! I think I have found a balance. But have I? Or is balance in itself a weasly compromise?

After a day's debate as I go to my little room, I am pursued by a male delegate with a visibly large erection pleading, as I try to slam my door, "But I need to communicate..."

At least I know how to translate that one.

It's the second day when Wilson Harris gets up to speak and questions are still vibrating angrily around the room. Harris is a big man, a handsome man, with natural dignity and gravitas, highly respected for his award-winning novels drawing on the myths of Guyana. Harris is not to be tampered with. Like a mountain, he is above the quarrels that we've been caught up in and he makes his own weather.

He starts, and speaks slowly, magisterially, in a rumbling considered Caribbean voice that has something of the necromancer. His rhetoric is not always easy. He has his own inner world that can be impenetrable. But when he comes to the question that has inflamed and nearly wrecked the conference, it's clear and sharp and simple and I sit up. He delivers a warning, straight as an arrow. He directs us back to Guyana, to the days of its struggle for independence. Very many artists saw where their duty lay, in being the voice of revolution and political action. In consequence a whole generation of creative artists was, he said, tragically lost. They had turned their backs on what was, he considered, their even deeper duty – to hear and speak from the depth of their own individual imagination. "I want to emphasise what appears to me to be the role of the creative imagination whether as painter, poet, artist, priest, scientist, craftsman. Down the centuries, one finds something invaluable in human terms which has always been threatened by pressures to conform to a monolithic convention or a monolithic tribalism."

I'm not sure what people around me are thinking, but I know that his words ring for me with authority. At the end of the day, they are all I can think about, and back in London after the whole event is over, they are what's lodging firmly in my mind. Where do I stand in terms of tribalism, commitment, race and identity? Have I accepted polarities too easily and glibly? Opposition is a heady place to be, but are there things of value that get lost in its sharp definitions? The imagination – as Harris says – is a slippery independent creature that lives outside manmade boundaries. But for me it is what makes ultimate sense. I feel uncomfortable, as if I may have missed an important pass.

It's late at night when I am sitting alone in Ledbury Road trying to write about CAM, my curtains shutting out the dark and the heavy non-stop rain outside. I can just hear the slap of steps on the wet street, and then they come up my stairs. It's Courtney, soaked to the bone. He stands in my small kitchen, shivering. His face and hair are shiny with rain and the water drips off him onto the lino. I go to speak to him, and then see his expression and stop. It is stunned but at the same time oddly elated.

"I was going home. I'd been at the Black House," he says, when he can speak. "And I was at the corner of All Saints Road, when I saw this old West Indian man. He was standing on the kerb, under a big old-fashioned umbrella. He kept putting one foot out to cross and then pulling it back again, when a car went speeding by. So I walked over and I took his arm. We waited together under his umbrella for a time, until it looked clear and I could steer him across. There was something about him. I can't say what. He was just a wizened little old man with white hair and thick spectacles. But as we finally made our way over the road, with the rain all noisy, bouncing on his umbrella, I had to talk to him – really talk to him about what was burning me up. I turned to him, and I asked him – 'Does it matter? Does it *really* matter?' And he looked up at me in the middle of the rain – just him and me and the wet night, and I said, 'Tell me – this black-white thing? Does it matter?'

"And he looked up at me with his faded old man's eyes and he said gently, 'No, son, it doesn't matter.' And then he repeated, so tranquilly, 'It doesn't matter. Not one bit.' And then he was gone."

Courtney turns around and rubs his eyes and he still looks a bit stunned. "I went to follow him but I couldn't see where he'd gone. You know, I think," he mutters, "I think he might have been the Angel Gabriel..."

I think he was only half joking.

We are both exhausted, or at least I know I am, by never-ending questions and the angry passions of the Grove that seem to be more and more toxic, turning in on and eating themselves like a snake. My Gabriel isn't Courtney's visitation but Wilson Harris, who has made me question my own moral compass. Our next issue of the *Hustler* mysteriously goes missing and the feeling on the street is sour. Who's still there to fight with me? And, at the end of the day, which fight?

"Come to India," says cartoonist friend Abu Abraham and his wife Sarojini, when I go over to have dinner at their place. After years in the west, they are packing up. England is too anti-immigrant and they want their daughters to grow up back 'home' in India. "You can stay with us."

"It's all yours," I say to Courtney, and I hand over all my *Hustler* files and copy for Hustler 5. I let my flat, pack my bags, and I leave.

PART THREE
MAKING MAPS

CHAPTER TEN
1970

" So did it work, going to India?" Lisa runs her finger absently along my windowsill as we wait for the kettle to boil.

Dust. I've haven't thought about dust, or about cleaning, for well over a year. An affable South Indian youth called Mani used to look after all that in Delhi. And there was the dhobi who called once a week and washed my clothes, and the chowkidar who tap-tap-tapped round the area at night, giving the occasional eerie whistle so householders who paid him to stay awake knew he's on the job.

All those invisible people propping me up, me and others. Briefly I think of the time when I was in a hotel room interviewing a group of maharajahs who'd come to Delhi to protest about having their princely stipends taken away. "Damned poor show!" they all agreed. One of them had bought a new tape recorder he wanted to show off, but the wall plug turned out to be shaky and the connection kept breaking. So he finally called a bearer, "Stand there with your foot against the plug," he instructed. So there he obediently stood, an elderly man, on one leg for what seemed hours while we were served *nimbu pani* (me) and *chota pegs* (them) and nodded to the strains of rumba and conga and pasa doble.

Did it work? Well, yes and no. And I wonder how I can tell even Lisa – my oldest and best friend – what those eighteen months had been like. The kettle jiggles about on the cooker and I pour water into two mugs of Nescafe. I am not sure I even know myself.

Images still run in my head.

I half wake up in the morning here in London and I sleepily wait for the sound of the early morning crows who wheel, cawing raucously, high over misty Delhi rooftops, but there's just the rumble of traffic on Westbourne Grove. I miss the acrid smoke rising from myriad small braziers, like a thousand little offerings. I even miss the shaggy night-watchmen, however much I curse their tap-tapping in the night, huddled up in their shawls outside the homes of the rich.

And so much more... Dog shows for the affluent – or rather, affluent dogs. Rajasthani women perching towers of bricks on wads of cloth folded onto their heads, and chattering.

The clubby companionability of it all – far more than I have ever felt in England: in Delhi's Press Club when the word went out that the khansama was making his famous kebabs; group forays into Old Delhi to buy fresh jelabis; driving in a carload, up in the hills for a cheery weekend in Simla. It all felt so jolly, almost like Angela Brazil grown up, and wonderfully protected. And back here, in Notting Hill? I'm surprised how lonely I feel.

"So you made it back. We all thought you'd stay there for ever."

"I had to come back. Didn't I tell you? The travel agent I went to in Delhi offered to throw in a reading of my astrological chart that said I'd come back..."

"So, what's it like being back? Are you pleased? Tell me everything!"

"It feels odd but not odd, if that doesn't sound too strange."

Everything looks the same but at the same time it feels different.

"When I went to get milk from the shop at the end of the road, I thought they'd be amazed and say "Where have you been?!" I was all prepared for that.. After all, I used to go in there every day and we'd always chat. But I don't think they even noticed they hadn't seen me for over a year. I know it's stupid."

"Not stupid at all," she says staunchly. "And we're putting out flags – every sort you'd like. It's jolly good to have you back. I just wish I was still living upstairs."

But she's not, and we both know that something has changed – that close female friendship, going back years. Lisa was my first and best real friend, way back when we were both eighteen in Birmingham. We'd both known immediately that we would get on when we first met. And so we have done, at the same college at Oxford, in our shared flat in Clapham and till recently right here in ramshackle Ledbury Road.

"I wish you were here still too."

"It was good, wasn't it?"

"How long have we known each other? Over ten years?"

Now we are twenty-six, almost half our lives. Well, give or take a few years.

It's not just the newsagent who's failed to hold his breath waiting for my return, or Lisa. I looked for Marvin and Raju and all the old Hustler crowd, but phone numbers have changed and nobody is the same in our old watering holes.

And now Lisa's gone, the most recent. The travel agent-astrologer said I'd nearly got married – true, till I discovered the poet wooing me was an alcoholic – and said that my time of conflict or 'mangal' would last till October. That's still months ahead. And in the meantime everyone but me is getting married and starting families. Lisa and Tim married while I was away ("How could you?!") and now there's a small Lucretia – Lisa tuts, *Lucasta* – a small Lucasta in the frame.

"But nice for you having your old friend Moira upstairs. She worked with you a while back in that little publishers, didn't she?"

But the way things are turning out – I won't tell Lisa this – I'm going to need friends and allies in the house. Right on cue, I couldn't have organised it better if I'd tried, there are sudden noises. Doors bang downstairs and footsteps sound running heavily down. Shouting.

"And don't you fucking come back!"

Lisa looks shocked, "Who? Goodness me!"

"That'll be Stacey."

"I think I met her. There was someone on the stairs when I came in – a young woman. Incredibly thin. Stick-like, really. She looked at me as if I was going to bite."

"That's her. They moved into Maureen's place downstairs her and Billy."

"Nice Maureen's gone?"

"Just like that."

The front door, two flights down, slams. The house shudders violently.

"She shouts all the time, but mostly at night. I think he beats her up. That's what it sounds like anyway."

"How dreadful!"

But it's worse than that. There's the blood and the needles in the bathroom. There're the people visiting late in the night. But I don't tell Lisa that.

"It's a shame about Maureen." We both got really fond of her – her high hectic colouring, her non-stop faith in men who were clearly chancers – the way she tried to damp herself down into what she thought was elegance, but under remained a good healthy country girl from Kerry. "Where's she gone?" Lisa asks.

"Who knows? Maybe back to Ireland."

"She was always talking about it. But we never thought she'd ever get round to it, did we? She and her cocktail cabinet." We smile at the memory. Black shiny plastic, it was: ruched with little gold studs, and back-lights at the top.

Lisa looks at her watch, "Is that the time? I've got to fly – I've got to pick up Lucasta or my mother-in-law will kill me." She starts to gather up her coat and bag. "But come over for a meal – you've hardly told me anything about India. Come over soon. Come over next week – Tim'll be away at a conference. I've still got to hear about what you got up to in 'Backside.'"

"Don't forget your present."

"As if! Lucasta'll *adore* the elephant. Thank you so much. You shouldn't have..."

"Call it 'Hatty'. Elephant in Hindi is 'hathi."

"You can teach her Indian when she gets older."

She puts the cloth elephant covered with mirror-work and spangles in her bag. We hug, and Lisa clatters downstairs in her high-heeled boots. The front door below closes. Not violently like Billy, but with a neat click.

It'd be morning now, in what Lisa accurately called 'Backside'. No. 8 Nizamuddin East (Backside) was its official address, to distinguish it from No. 8 Nizamuddin East (Frontside), except that they never needed to use the term 'Frontside', because Frontside was the real thing. Backside just hid behind Frontside as a sort of secret annexe.

To reach Backside, you needed to follow Frontside's wall into the side street and an unmarked door set into a garden wall. Inside, a long path led under an arch of jasmine all the way down to my quiet one-storey apartment. A tunnel of jasmine – who could ever resist such a thing?

Sometimes I'd just carry on walking up the tree-lined road, shaded by gulmohurs, to the great marble and sandstone tomb for Emperor Humayun, set back behind wide formal gardens. This is my territory, Muslim territory, Nizamuddin. It is steeped in Islam. It exudes a sense of certainty and acceptance. The tombs, all so confident and quiet and old – not only the emperor's but also his uncle Akbar's: none of them fenced off and ticketed as they would be in the west, where they'd be shut away as 'national treasures'. Here they just hang around, as part of the furniture, of ongoing life, like an old grandfather living with you in the house. I sit and soak up their calm and certainty.

But this is London. I sigh and go to wash up our coffee mugs under the cold tap in the corner basin. One day maybe I'll get a geyser. Hot water would be nice. Lisa always leaves a bustle in the air behind her. It's like the way trees go on vibrating after a strong wind.

Teach her Indian, bless her. I wish.

Language didn't really matter in Delhi. Everyone I knew seemed to have come from somewhere else in India anyhow, so they spoke Bengali or Marathi or whatever. And because they were from that sort of class, they'd have been sent to 'English medium' schools anyhow and sometimes had been to university in the west. But language isn't the only thing. Language isn't just words.

"How about this one," says Sushila, as we all sit outside a cafe in Connaught Circus and she hums a tune. "Mere samne wale!"

Krishan and Omar and Anjana shout at the same time, "Parosan!" and everyone laughs.

I don't know the films. I don't have the memories. I don't have the attitudes either. I fret when men – even the intelligentsia – so easily take precedence as if that's the most natural thing in the world, and how easily women slot themselves into place beside (or behind) them.

Visiting relatives deep in rural Madhya Pradesh where Abba was born, we all go out to visit a local beauty spot as the day's stifling heat starts to die down. My two distant cousins climb into the front of the large dusty Land Rover. Into the back we clamber: three aunts, a female family servant, half a dozen assorted children and me. In order to preserve our modesty, a thick black cloth is let down between front seats and back seats.

It is hot in the back, the heat is oppressive and there are many of us crammed into a small window-less space. In the spacious front loll Cousin 1 and Cousin 2, talking of visits to ice-cream parlours. They are plump young blades who wear shiny western suiting and imitation Italian shoes with winkle-picker toes, and I came to resent them more and more as the Land Rover bounces over pitted roads and in the back we jiggle and shriek.

"That's the way things should be," says Abba when I go back home and recount my travels, and I think I see a glint of satisfaction in his eye. He likes the fact that I have been corralled for once into satisfactory Muslim-daughter behaviour.

Back home after all that time, it takes a little while to slot into daughter mode. They both look smaller and older. Mother wants to hear about horror stories now, as if it confirms her current view of a place she considers has brought her nothing but problems: inefficiency, muddle, corruption, feuding, dirt.

"Now, Gerda," says Abba uneasily, rubbing the back of his dry hand with the other, which is always a sign that he is uncomfortable. "You know that's not true. It wasn't like that..."

"Ach, dirty place. Just as well you're back home again, where you belong."

"You know your mother – she has strong feelings," says Abba when mother has left the room with a flounce. "She doesn't mean it."

He goes to fetch his walking stick and scarf. "Come along. I haven't had my walk."

"She doesn't understand India. She's never been there. Of course she doesn't understand."

But as I talk I can tell that even my India is not Abba's India either. I describe visiting the vast bulk of the Diwan Mahal, the family's ancestral home in Seoni. To me, it was melancholy and odd. A complex of old buildings marooned behind a postern in a big medieval gate, half deserted and in great need of repair. But while it makes me think of Chekhov, Abba, I am sure, thinks of childhood.

"And the family graveyard there – with the last family elephant!"

He doesn't get that either. To him, a family elephant means lack of progress. Nothing to boast about, better keep it quiet. A Citroen or an Austin Sunbeam maybe, even better, a Jaguar, that would be fine. But an elephant? No question, I am transfixed by the thought that I am related in a manner of speaking to an elephant. Abba sweeps it aside.

But I have done some things he approves of. He's pleased that I met maharajahs and that I went to the grand Rashtrapati Bhavan to interview the President's wife, even though he would have preferred me to have interviewed the President. I had puzzled the aides too. "Why do you want to speak with her?" they said. "She is just an ordinary Indian housewife – she looks after her household, she does the cooking."

"And in Bombay," I chatter on, "I was friends with Farida who's sister of Dilip Kumar – you know, the film star, the most popular one in India. They invited me to stay with them out at their beach place out at Juhu." This doesn't hit the spot in the same way with Abba as the President. Hindi film-stars, I remember, are morally suspect. But I have a card that can rescue this.

"You know, of course, that Dilip's real name is Yusuf – he's really Yusuf Khan, he changed his name because it was better to have a Hindu name when he started out. Not a Muslim name." Abba can understand those barriers and no-go areas. He was the one to caution me when I flew to India. "Watch out," he said. "When you go through Customs, make sure you don't go to a Sikh official. They hate Muslims..." And then there was Julia Masters.

I was right – Islam outweighs the *filmi* lifestyle. He grunts.

"That's good. Keep up with them. You don't know what it might lead to..."

I know that this means we are approaching dangerous ground, and indeed it is so. Here, it comes...

"Now you are back, what are your plans?"

It sounds casual, but I recognise an implacable undertone that's long familiar. We reach the end of the rec, where it meets Manor House Lane, and he wheels around in a sharp military manner. We double back on our tracks.

I hedge. "Well, I'll need to get myself settled. Then I'll get in touch with a few magazines.."

"I've been thinking. Can't you go back to those publishers you worked for? That was a good job, steady."

"I like what I'm doing," I say defensively.

He tuts impatiently.

"Like? That's got nothing to do with it. Where's the future? Your mother and I won't be here for ever, and..."

"I'm alright, Abba, really..."

"And that, that place you're living in. Don't interrupt! Your mother told me about it. Not even any hot water! You can't go on like that. Don't forget you're thirty now. You're not a spring chicken any longer."

He jabs his stick into the soft soil of the rec.

"Get a property. I'll help you. Anwar's got his own place now he's qualified as a lawyer. I bought it for him while you were away – a nice bungalow outside Bristol. I'll help you. I can afford it."

I've been away and nothing's changed, I think through gritted teeth. That's always his answer – properties, properties. Properties and possessions.

"Look around – somewhere like South Kensington..."

South Kensington? I bite my tongue. At that moment I am prepared to fight to the death to remain in my two rooms in Notting Hill, cold water or not. Forever. Who cares about such things? No hot water? There's kettles, aren't there?

Finally – "The best thing would be for you to get married. You can marry anyone now. You can chose who you want, I won't mind – you can even marry..." He thinks hard, "An African."

That's it, I think.

But the train back is late and the 27 bus from Paddington takes an age to come and the seediness around the late-night station isn't free and joyous at all. Notting Hill seems to have lost the buoyant spirit it had had before I left too. I look around in vain for my old life. Where is everyone? Marvin is nowhere to be seen, and I never knew where he lived anyway. I wander past the Rio, but it's closed, and along Westbourne Park Road looking for signs of the mocking graffiti that had been scrawled on

Courtney's wall after our Observer interview – 'No white cat can talk for a black cat.' No cats here, black or white: no Courtney. Nor, I know, will there be. I find a few people from before, but everyone is in a hurry. Here's Vince, one of the cleverest in the Grove and also one of angriest. He has signed up to go to college, he says, as a mature student, and looks oddly – for Vince – happy. For a moment it feels as if all the radicalism was a holiday thing, and now people have dusted out their uniforms and have gone back to school. Michael X's Black House has, I hear, burned down.

So where's the bravado that I displayed with Abba? It's very hard to rekindle now I am back in my one-person flat. Somehow I've got to get back into earning my living. I was doing all right before I left. I look back on the figures for 1969 – I'd made £1,545 pounds, nineteen shillings and twopence. Not bad. More than I'd earned at my first job in Max Parrish. I can live on £1,545/19/2d. The rent takes £240 a year and the owners have never put it up – we're probably too small fry. So where can I save? I see I spent just under £100 on travel, and that was the biggest item, twice as much as telephone rental. Well, I could walk more.

But what if I don't get commissions? I suppose I could cut down on books – £37 pounds, four shillings and ninepence – that's quite a lot. And I could send the television back and save £20 hire fee a year. It never worked well anyway.

The astrologer in India warned me that my bad 'mangal' time was predicted to last till the end of the year. But then life would get brighter. And marriage he said was on the cards, to someone who would adore me and say, "Yes, darling, it is the moon," if I insisted that that the daytime sun was the moon. I don't see this is great for a relationship, but ah, the thought of someone being there for me!

It's all do-able. So why do I feel so miserable?

I miss Courtney. When I said I was leaving, he told me that he'd found a flat in St Stephens's Square where we could live together. I couldn't help grimacing. What irony, what timing! I've always hankered after St Stephen's Square, its faded elegance and wrought-iron balconies. Too late. I was exhausted and spikey, manic, confusing, depressive, lonely. Courtney was not what I needed. And Courtney? Even if he was around, I know his pride wouldn't let him deal in re-runs.

While I've been away, it looks as if lines and politics have got harder too. The hang-out café up the Portobello has become the Black People's Information Centre. Frank Critchelow's Rio coffee bar at the end of my road has moved and is now the Mangrove, and a Community Association and being constantly harassed by the local police. Even our Hustler's resident poet has changed his name to an African one and disappeared behind the doors of the small African-oriented centre he's set up. I think back to the broad-based meetings in the People's Centre and even the Hustler and its aim to speak for a whole community.

But the summer's lovely, so coming back from Delhi is cushioned. I keep all my windows open and fresh un-London summer breezes come wafting in with bursts of Beatles played non-stop by a fan in a nearby flat. I look out on hippies drifting gently in flowing clothes and it feels as if there is a truce in the street. Lisa's gone, but Moira is still in the little flat under the roof.

I'll leave it to the autumn and then I'll take all the invoices and receipts out from the drawer where I routinely shove them.

Autumn comes and I take a deep breath. The drawer looks quite full, so maybe things are better than I'd thought. I tip it all out. I had a few pieces in the Guardian and New Society and one in The Times. But the bulk, it turns out, is a thick transcript of a broadcast about the status of women that I'd been part of and that runs to a lot of pages.. OK, let's put that aside, and add up the figures.

Not good. Since I got back – that's four months in all – I've made a grand total of £300. It looks as if the astrologer was right, and the bad *mangal* time is still here.

Moira is a sceptic when I tell her about this and far less impressed than I am,

"Och," she says with a mild Scottish scoff, "You surely can't believe in all that rubbish!"

"No, of course not... But still, Moira, he did get some things right." I can see she doesn't believe me. "He knew I was born on a Friday, and that I've got a mother with a hot temper and breathing problems. And he said I have a younger brother who's headstrong, which is most certainly true."

I think I will leave out the prediction of a marriage to a doting older man, because I really want to believe in the bit about the end of the *mangal* which is due in only two months' time.

I can hang on for that.

CHAPTER ELEVEN
1972

To be quite honest, I am not as chipper as I make out. Money is running out and work is thin. The people at 'Education Magazine' haven't even responded to my application to be assistant editor. Ed Victor and Richard Neville are planning a new underground paper to be called 'Ink'. "Come and talk," they say, but there is no job. I sleep poorly and have vivid dreams. I dream of being marooned on the top of a mountain – the people who've led me there have abandoned me. If I take even one step, I will fall. Where is everyone? I am finding it hard to breathe. At other times, I wake in the depths of the night convinced I have found the answer to everything. At one point it is so compelling that I switch on the light and carefully write it down: 'The cast of the worm is its form. The thing to remember is that *there is no separation*, no real struggle. Here is the well, here are the people around it. Both are there. No people without the well.' Well, that's a lot of help, I think in the light of common day.

In the day it is hard to pick up the phone for even a simple phone call. Words come slowly and mostly I reject what I was about to say before I have finished saying it. I smoke quantities of Silk Cut, choosing the 'less harmful' cigarette,wondering why I bother.

It's like going back to the dark days when David's letter came telling me he was going to get married to someone else. I wish I still had the pills that I was finally given because I couldn't stop weeping. I cling to the astrologer's prediction, at least in public – "Only another month or two and then I'll be rich," I quip to Lisa – but I really know that it is nothing but moonshine. It's pathetic, worse than pathetic – that I give house-room to a cut-rate prediction thrown in as a sweetener by a backstreet Delhi travel-agent. How could I even be so stupid?

"How about the jobs column in *Time Out*?" suggests Moira, passing the new magazine over, when I go up to her place for a cup of Nescafe.

"It doesn't look much use." I run my finger along the sparse Jobs column. "I could sell candles, or here's one for a DJ, someone to play records in a Holland Park discotheque." Holland Park – not my scene.

"I can't see myself doing this either... Listen – 'Fleet Street producer requires young good-looking girls with very good figure for glamour/nude bikini etc modelling .World wide advertising and the odd film production...'"

"Better stick with the candles," advises Moira.

"I'm too fat anyway."

"*Time Out* needs an office cleaner." Safer, but I'm no good at cleaning. "And, oh, this is the pits: 'Commission paid for introducing customers to our range of telephone answering machines'. Oh, Moira, I don't think I could *bear* to spend my days demonstrating telephone answering machines!"

"There are worse things in life, you know," she says a bit tartly.

But when I take the magazine down to my own flat, I go on nosing through it. *Time Out* didn't exist when I let for India, and though it is very small and a fortnightly, I can see it has more to it than ads for semi nude good-looking ladies and answering machines. The more I see, the more I like it. I approve of the people who self-advertise. They have a sense of hope, even though it's a bit daft. 'I paint mandalas', 'Book my Happy Vans'. Vivienne – a 'communication-starved chick' – is looking for a 'Head Commune'. A Kensington centre offers a focus on 'a higher evolution of consciousness' with chanting to follow; and there are quantities of demos – against the Immigration Bill, apartheid, the Bomb. There's underground music, and dance and sculpture at Middle Earth.

It is so long since I looked out over the walls of the Grove. Now that I do, I rather like the look of the landscape. It is like a slightly dotty carnival and makes me think of Formentera when I tumbled into the baby days of the summer of love. But in between all the froth and the posturing and the absurdity there is something definitely attractive.

"They still want to change the world," I tell Moira. And so, of course, do I.

And now, here was feisty little *Time Out* waiting for me, providing signposts to a different sort of London. I pick it up regularly now. And a few weeks later in the new issue I see something that brings me up short. I look again. Have I made a mistake? I tumble up the short flight to Moira's attic eyrie.

"Look!" I brandish *Time Out*.

In a section called 'Theatreboard', the section's editor, John Ford, is complaining about the numbers of new Fringe theatres. They are increasing at such a rate, he says, it's got to the point when he can't manage to cover them all. So... he wants to find an assistant. "If you're interested, send in sample reviews of three recent shows you've seen..."

Time Out's offices are in a crumbling tall building just across from Kings Cross station, with Mole Records on one side and a South Indian restaurant on the other. It is crumbly and short-life, and so thin that all the rooms are stacked on top of each other like a tower of children's bricks. I climb up and up in search of the Theatre Section.

"Just keep on going," says the cheerful woman on Reception down on the ground floor. "You'll find it." It seems all stairs and perilous coconut matting with holes in it. On each floor I find a few rooms ("No, Theatre's upstairs..."), and I plough on up. I am here to be interviewed but it feels increasingly unlikely. Everybody looks very young. I'm thirty three – maybe they'll think I'm too old?

But it doesn't turn out like that. John Ford, who's wrestling with a long strip of galley proofs, seems mildly surprised to see me even though he'd fixed the time himself,

"Oh hello," he says cheerfully, "I'd forgotten you were coming in this morning, just clear a chair and sit down. I'll be with you in a minute once I get rid of these wretched things..."

He's not what I expected. I thought he'd be cool and editor-like, and was expecting to have to show him my cuttings book. But he's cheerful and relaxed, with an easy rather soft quality, and he treats me as if I've been around forever. This is nice, but I begin to wonder if he's forgotten that I've applied for the job too.

"There," he finally says and he pushes the typewriter and papers to one side. "That's done till the next issue. Now we can relax. I'm sorry about that." He doesn't really sound sorry. "Thank you for coming in. I'm afraid," he looks around vaguely, "There's not much space."

True. The desk and the floor are overflowing with programmes and press releases and posters and books and letters. He gets up and moves them over to one corner. "But we can clear a bit of space over here for you, I think. I suppose you'll need a typewriter?"

"You mean –" I hardly dare say this, "I've got the job?"

"Oh yes, of course. Didn't I say? I was sure I'd said that on the telephone. No question. You were much the best of everyone who applied, by far the best. You know it's part-time – three days a week. That's alright, I hope?" He beams at me in a friendly but hopeful fashion.

"So you see," I phone Lisa to tell her, "It proves it – astrology works!"

"There is one special weapon that black actors have..."

Hovhaness Pilikian is about to induct me into the secrets of his black theatre group, the Cervantes Players. I sit up with my pencil poised.

This could be the nub of the feature I'm writing. What could the special weapon be? Surely not a particular physicality? African roots? The edge born out of oppression and resistance? I lean forward.

Pilikian likes the tension of the pause, theatre-man that he is. He's a voluble thick set Armenian, and I suspect is currently teasing me.

"Can you think what?"

I shake my head. He waits.

"It's... their teeth!"

"Their teeth?"

This is not what I'd expected.

He nods, pleased at my reaction,

"Yes, I am the only one to have discovered that! Look..." He beckons to a very tall and very dark-skinned company member and calls him over from the other end of the rehearsal room. "Smile!" he instructs. The man obeys and a sudden slash of pure dazzling white cuts across the inky blackness of his face. It is disconcertingly like a party trick.

"Hovhaness Pilikian thinks the thing about black actors is their teeth," I tell John Ford when I get back to the Gray's Inn Road.

He looks mildly startled.

"Well, that's a new angle... I remember he was particularly interested in work with masks."

"Yes, that too."

"Still, it's given me a thought – it's about time we do something about black theatre. Let's bring it up in the editorial conference."

I'm just beginning to understand the workings of *Time Out*. The way we are all stacked separately on top of each other in the crumbling building is perfect. We aren't a magazine: we are a federation. One section under Chris Petit knows everything about film and independents and co-operatives. The Agit-Prop writers have their own uncompromising political stance. The Sell Out section, run by lovely Lindsay Barham, searches out best buys and trendiest places to eat. It is a ragbag of passions.

But we have one thing in common. We all haggle for more space each week with our editor, Tony Elliott. And more and more. It makes no difference that Time Out's changed its format. It was a neat little booklet you could slip in your pocket when I came back to London. Now it's grown to standard magazine size and put on pages. But every week the cry goes up – give us more space!

"A new lunch-time theatre in Soho," John announces on Monday morning, "Above a pub in Brewer St. They're calling it the Act Inn."

"That must be near the Little Theatre, you know the one up all those stairs off St Martin's Lane?"

"No, it's just round the corner from the Almost Free Theatre."

"Not near the Open Space then?"

If we had a map, flags for little theatres would be scattered all over London – from Barnet to Turnham Green, Richmond to Hackney. They are exploding, mushrooming everywhere – in pubs and bookshops, libraries and warehouses. We run them to earth in car-parks or in the street as Agit-Prop, down the underground as Tube Theatre, on the canal as Mikron Theatre.

"How about reviewing this show in a phone box?" asks John.

"Are you serious?"

He smiles enigmatically. It must be a joke. But it's not.

"The thing is," he says approvingly, as we sit drinking our coffee, "Theatre is the most accessible art form. Think about it. What do you need? Just two things – people and a space. That's it. You don't need special equipment like film or a formal building. You don't need years of training like dancers do. You don't even have to have a script. You can just do it."

I glow. I feel proud to be at the cutting edge of invention, here in the very best bit of Time Out. Late at night I sit at home when Notting Hill is quiet and write about wild improvised pieces and shows that poke their complacent audiences and ones that take over strange spaces and ones that jettison words and actors descend like missiles swooping down from unexpected shrouded heights. Five nights a week, and sometimes at lunchtime too – no wonder John needed a deputy.

"Here's an interesting one for you," he says. "'Lay By' – Portable Theatre, seven writers who've each written a short play inspired by the same rather gruesome news event. David Hare, Snoo Wilson, Steven Poliakoff..."

"For a caption review?"

"No. It's interesting work. I saw it up in Edinburgh. We'll do a longer review."

"Fine."

"And why don't you follow up Hovhaness and check out the Dark and Light? I'll go up and have a word with Tony about giving us space for a feature."

It's not easy finding the Dark and Light Theatre. The streets in Brixton are lined with small Victorian terrace houses. I wander up and down streets and streets of them with hardly even a shop in sight, let alone a theatre. It feels domestic and private. Children are coming home from

Amma and Abba, 1935

Naseem, 1943

Abba and Amma at Buckingham Palace c.1965

Naseem, right, with dance group

Naseem, second from right and U.S. Krishna Rao second from left
with his wife Chandrabhaga Devi in the middle

Naseem and Anwar

Naseem and George 1980

Naseem with OBE

Naseem Khan 2008 © George Torode

Nassem in East End on Arnold Circus

school and the working day's beginning to wind down. When I pass the occasional person, I have the feeling they look at me sideways. I am white and a stranger and I stick out. Eventually, I give up and ask for directions, but nobody has heard of a Dark and Light Theatre. Or even a theatre.

Finally a young man with braids stops and thinks a bit and then says, "I think there's something going on in the Longfield Hall... Just round the corner."

I turn and go back on my tracks. I'd passed it without noticing. The Dark and Light must be the most understated theatre in London. Longfield Hall was built as a local authority hall for municipal events. Though it looks shut up, I can still catch a whiff of something old-fashioned and solid, election hustings and prize-givings and planning consultations.

I am late. When I get there, Frank Cousins and his colleague Manley Young are clearly waiting for me on the other side of the swing doors. Of course I lie when Cousins asks, "I hope you found it easily?" The two men couldn't be more different – Cousins is large and handsome with a grand actor's resonant voice; his personality rolls over Young who is small and spry, with the congenitally cautious air of a natural admin man.

But they are in accord. "Here we are," declares Cousins proudly. "After a long, long search, The Dark and Light Theatre. The perfect building and the perfect location, in the heart of the black community."

"After all the trouble we had to go through," puts in Young, "To get the local Council to let us have the use of it."

"Months and months of them putting up obstacles, changing their minds."

"Not to mention the Arts Council." They lead the way proudly through the tiled foyer, still with noticeboards for long ago civic events. "And here," says Cousins, "Is the auditorium," and he opens double doors with a flourish. The hall is big. It is institutional. High windows at each side and a high stage at one end and a level floor. No rostra or raked seating to make it easy to see what's happening on stage. I don't know what to say. All I can see are problems. I suspect the acoustics are awful. "Wow," I say and that seems to do for now.

Our steps echo on the polished floor. We study the stage. "Athol Fugard's 'The Blood Knot' is going to be our first production. We're ready to go into rehearsal now."

"Now that the Arts Council has agreed. They've given us a £1,000 grant to put on a season of plays. We know that we have a challenge on our hands in reaching audiences," acknowledges Young. "We don't have a theatre tradition in Jamaica, or the West Indies. We are going to have to work hard."

"It's a wonderful opportunity." Cousins cuts across him. "We're going to let black actors cut their teeth on good roles, major roles, for a change. Not minor parts or spear-carriers."

"Or thugs or criminals."

"Now we can get going. And after that our next show will be, 'Emperor Jones' by Eugene O'Neill."

A big play – the story of the flawed African American who led a doomed slave uprising.

"Wasn't it on at Edinburgh a few years back?" I remember.

"That's right – James Earl Jones played Brutus Jones. And before that it was Paul Robeson. It's a wonderful part – one of the few substantial parts for black actors." Cousins squares up visibly – I can see it, I can see Brutus Jones.

"One of the very few substantial roles." Young agrees.

£1,000 for a season, I jot in my notebook.

"So you're going to encourage new writing?"

"We'll have to. Where are the scripts? Where are the roles? Where's work showing our experience as black people here in Britain?"

"And we will write our own," says Young. "At Christmas we're planning to do a pantomime based on Anansi. Everyone knows Anansi and loves Anansi."

Anansi – the cunning spider of folk myth who finds a way round every difficulty. A good friend to have on your side.

I fill my notebook and leave them to their plans. I slowly wander back along the maze of back streets, thinking hard. The challenge they've taken on – that lumbering hall, an audience to be wooed. And they are right. We didn't think of discrimination in the arts when we ran the Hustler – it was all about housing and jobs. But where *are* the roles? Or the scripts or the opportunities? How often have I seen black actors on stage? Or, for that matter, on television? All the confident young companies and groups I've been reviewing – apart from Hovhaness – have been white.

"Maybe they don't want to do theatre?" Moira says sensibly. "You can't force people. And if the parts are not there?" she asks, putting down the proofs she's been correcting.

"Mmm," I am not convinced. "We're so certain the arts are alright – no racism and everyone's equal. But just look at the evidence."

"It feels all wrong, Moira, Frank and Manley struggling away down there in that awful place. White actors don't have to struggle that way. It's hard to put my finger on it. But it's as if they are on their home turf."

"Well," Moira considers, "It reminds me," she goes on, "of something that happened to Renee. You know my sister, Renee..."

"Who teaches in a primary school in Brixton?"

"When it was the elections, her class asked her all sorts of questions about them. So in the end she said they'd hold their own to see how it works. She gave all the kids voting slips and told them to vote for one person in the class to be prime minister and one to be deputy.

"Renee's class is almost entirely West Indian. There are only two or three white children. When she got to count up the votes, she was shocked. The class had chosen the white children to be prime minister and deputy."

"Oh... Were they particularly popular?"

"Not at all. Quite the opposite. Renee said they were actually quite nondescript."

Outside the light is fading and Moira needs to get back to the manuscript she is editing. I sigh and pick up my things. As I head downstairs to my flat, I think about the *Hustler* days and the time we pulled down the fences round Powis Square. The exhilaration. Defeating discrimination seemed so simple then. Or so we thought. Just identify the enemy, join forces and take action.

And I wonder about Abba and his doctor peers – their resolutely faux British style. The rose beds, mock Tudor and their smart suits. How determined Abba'd been to distance himself from the Punjabi villagers who arrived later.

"Fences erected in your head," I write in my diary, and look at the words. "Far more difficult to pull down?"

"One for you," says Mandy from Agit-Prop, dropping a cyclostyled leaflet on my desk on her way downstairs. The Fasimbas? Never heard of them. It's an invitation to a Sunday evening of sketches in Brixton – and, oh no, they're hiring Longfield Hall...

"Well, it's not going to be exactly overwhelming," I tell John with certainty. "A few loyal supporters in an empty hall." At least I know the way there now.

Sunday night in Brixton however is more lively than it was in the doldrums of a mid-weekday afternoon. But then, turning the corner, I stop. Can I be in the right place? There are crowds there, crowds – almost entirely black – massing around the entrance to the Longfield Hall. There are stewards, sharp young men and young Afro-haired women, all in dark shades and black military Panther-style berets, trying to marshal the crowds. There's good-natured pushing and shoving and laughter.

It's hard to find a spare place to sit. The rows are taken up with whole families – well-dressed mothers, hordes of children, smart fathers in suits, aunties and grandmothers. The babble of noise and conversation is tremendous, hardly hushing when the curtain finally goes up. We are watching a series of sketches – the first ones are about slavery and there's a bit of shifting and yawning around me. But then they turn into sketches about local life and I can slowly feel a ripple of recognition running through the audience, and people start nudging and whispering to each other. Then it takes off.

They are broad satirical sketches. There's the pastor who is siphoning off donations for his own benefit. There are whoops of laughter, "Oh my Lord!" People around me slap their thighs. There's the stuck-up lady who's so proud of her h'English style. There are people back home in the Caribbean, talking of their future in London where the streets just have to be paved with gold. "True, man!" At times the laughter is so intense that the cast – who are amateur – have to stop and wait because they can't be heard.

And then comes a scene that goes even closer home. The curtain goes up on a sitting room. Parents are castigating their two teenage children for joining a campaign against racism and police harassment. "Don't you get involved," command the parents hotly. "It's dangerous – you could get arrested! What about your future then?" We are clearly heading for a major showdown – anger, recriminations, walk out. But, no. Instead the children face it head on. They explain just why they needed to make a commitment. They remind their parents – gently – of the racism they had met and they make it clear they are fighting for them too. They have to do it, they say. It is dignity. Self-worth. The hall falls silent and the whooping dies away. The parents and aunties and grandparents sit still. They are all listening.

At the end there's a reflective stirring and a pause and then applause breaks out. It rolls on, wave after wave and the cast stand there looking young and uncertain and happy. I sit on my metal chair, moved nearly to tears by the generosity of what I have witnessed and – rough though it was – by the power of theatre to hit truth. The imagination, I think, That is what can bind us. That is what can transform. Wilson Harris was right. I feel suddenly larger and unaccountably happy.

I slide out and make my way home through the now dark streets, the Longfield Hall blazing with lights behind me. I can't stop humming, tunelessly.

CHAPTER TWELVE
1973

I can see Mother before she sees me. She's standing on the balls of her feet and trying to spot me over the heads of the crowds milling around the station complex. She's wearing what I think they call a 'car coat' and she's had her hair dyed a sort of blond-copper colour: it's set in careful waves.

"Yes, there's a new place in town Mrs Simmons in my Ikebana class told me about," she says happily, as she steers the car out of the crowded station car-park.

For as long as I can remember Mother's gone to the old-fashioned salon down the road and Joyce has been doing her hair. When I was little they let me sit on a stool and play with the plastic rollers while Amma sat under one of the big hoods until her perm dried, and her face got all red and I had to shout to make her hear me. And now Mother has turned her back on Joyce and the salon. It feels a bad move. If I had my way, she would stay just as she had been twenty years ago when she was cosy and cuddly and never worried about fashion or smart hairdressers. Or if she did, I never knew about it. But even so, maybe it's a good sign? Maybe the gulf between her and Abba that had been so painful has healed.

"It's the latest place," she's saying. "But the prices they charge! Of course I suppose it's nothing compared to what you're used to in London, but it's quite a shock for our little Birmingham."

Her crisp unnatural hair-do slightly shakes as we career around the Digbeth roundabout and weave between the traffic on the Coventry Road.

"You'll have to be quiet," she warns as she parks the car in our driveway. "He's got a meeting about the mosque. They're in the sitting room." There's a mild mumble of male voices as we creep past the closed door, down the hall to the breakfast room.

Mother puts the kettle on in the kitchen and takes out her pack of cigarettes. "Would you like one?"

"Better not." I glance nervously in the direction of the sitting room.

And sure enough, her cigarette isn't half smoked when there's the noise of departures. "Khuda hafiz," go loud voices as one after the other they depart and the front door closes after each one. It sounds like an army is leaving.

We sit there as quiet as mice.

But when Abba's seen off the very last, Mother, with a practised move, tosses her cigarette out of the window. She knows exactly how long she's got.

Abba appears not to notice, but I'm glad I didn't accept Mother's offer. He'd have been sure to have noticed the smell.

But he's also tired.

"Tea, Gerda," he says heavily and sits down at the table by the window. "Good meeting?"

"Too much talk. Nothing but talk, talk. Everybody wanting to be the top dog. That's the trouble with our people."

"I told you not to get involved," she scolds. (Ah, they are back to normal...) "You knew what it's going to be like. Remember the trouble you had with the other doctors when you wanted to dissolve the partnership?"

He ignores her.

"They want me to become secretary of the mosque committee."

Mother sighs.

"Here we go," she rolls her eyes.

"I would rather be Chairman," he admits candidly "But Rizvi wanted that."

He sips his tea, "I'll show you the plans," he tells me. "You'll like to see them because you're artistic."

The plans are grand. Very grand. They slightly scare me. The little terrace house that was the mosque was so discreet. It was modest and didn't advertise itself. It was like all those community halls where we spent time for Indian Association events, our secret. You had to know where it was to find them.

This mosque is going to dominate the skyline. It's an in-your-face mosque. There'll be no missing it.

"It's awfully big, Abba."

"Not big enough. We need to think big," he says happily. "There'll be facilities for not one but two prayer halls, and accommodation for ladies too."

"Won't it be terribly expensive? Where will you get the money?"

"Saudi Arabia will help. We've got a meeting at the embassy next week."

Abba is wheeling and dealing and how he loves it. "And this is where the education wing will go. And here, on the third floor, we'll have rooms for visiting imams and scholars..."

And then he folds the plans up carefully and briskly changes the subject.

"Now, what about you? Any news?"

This has to mean marriage, but fortunately I have an alternative bit of information.

"I'm thinking about leaving *Time Out*. I've been offered another job."

He puts down his cup.

"I went for a meeting with the Arts Council the other day. They want me to do a study, sort of research. They don't know about immigrants and if they have culture that the Arts Council maybe should know about. Y'know, music and dance and so on."

He is not impressed.

"That's not a full-time job. You can do that in your spare time, in the evening or at weekends. No need to give up the *Time Out* for that."

"That's exactly what the Arts Council people said. They said I could do it part-time, and that it would take less than six months. And I could keep on at *Time Out*."

"They know what they are talking about," he says approvingly. "Listen to them. They're the experts."

I think back to all the hidden events – scores of them – I encountered when we danced for all those Indian associations all over the country, and I wonder. Really? Only six months, and part-time?

"Why does it always have to be immigrants with you?" Mother tuts, "Like that dreadful newspaper you were involved with – what was it called? Can't you do something English for a change?

"She's always got to be *different*," she complains to the world.

"I don't know if I should do it. Anyway, I said I'd think about it."

And then I pull out my ace. "Oh, by the way, next time I come home I'd like to bring a friend for you to meet."

There's a sudden hopeful silence.

"His name is John. He's a Guardian journalist." I almost add, triumphantly, "And he's English," but then I decide to be good.

And after that I can do no wrong.

I have gravitated towards immigrants rather than the English; the arts rather than law (as Anwar's done) or medicine – but no matter. I am bringing a man home – the first since David, whom they wouldn't accept – and their relief is palpable. She says,

"You must tell me what your John likes to eat before you come."

As I leave to get my train back to London, Abba finally says in a wheedling voice,

"Find a property. It's the time. I'll give you the deposit." And I finally say maybe and we are finally friends. It seems an opportune moment to mention something else I've had in mind for some time. "By the way, If John and I drive up, would you mind if I take Bambi back? I'd really like to have him in my place."

"Yes, of course." he says with a large and lordly gesture. "Naturally. Anything you want."

It feels odd, not having to go to the theatre after all those years of reviewing almost nightly for Time Out. I potter around my flat, fiddling, making cups of coffee I don't really need. I suppose in time, I'll get used to it. I could spend some time looking through estate agents' papers, though there's nothing there that I really like. And there is the questionnaire to sort out for the new minority arts report I've finally agreed to write, though full time and certainly not a few days a week...

Then the phone rings. It's John. Good. "What are you doing? How about coming to see the new Scorsese? It's on at Hampstead."

"Well. I don't know... I should be working. I've got my advisory committee meeting next week. But, oh well, yes – OK."

I can hear John's low-slung MG with its distinctive roar when he's still a few streets away. He parks with a dash – a rarity in Ledbury Road where we normally run to rather old Austins or Morris Minors – and bounds upstairs. He is in his rumbustious Tigger mood and hardly winces as he passes the dark bathroom at the bend of the stairs because he's talking loudly about the press conference at the TUC he's just been to. "Fucking wankers!"

"Shh!" I hiss as we pass Billy and Stacy's door.

"Oh, bugger them!" he explodes. "It's a free country. I can say what I like, can't I?"

I bustle him upstairs and safely inside. He can sometimes be very noisy. His clothes are noisy too. Today he is wearing white bell bottoms covered with green stars and stripes; his shirt is red. But there's something really engaging about his utter full-on quality, even down to the noise.

"If he was a wine," I say to Lisa, "He'd be marked 'full-bodied.'"

"You mean he's fat?"

"No! Well, only a little... I mean, in spirit.

"And he knows so much, and he's really good at explaining things. I think I almost understand inflation now."

Even the car's exhaust explodes noisily as we fart away from Ledbury Road.

The film over, we troop out of the cinema into the night air, one pair amongst many busily chattering couples,

"Hungry? Let's go for a curry."

It feels such a comfortable cliché, so familiar but forgotten: so far from Ledbury Road. The lamb dopiaza and matter paneer and channa masala arrive.

"You remember I ordered extra hot?"

The waiter reassures him,

"Oh yes sir, *very* hot."

We sit and dissect Scorsese and the Heath government and Clause 4. It's like being in an alternative universe. I like it and yet don't like it at one and the same time. It's oddly restful, even though John is the least restful of men.

"How's your house hunting going? Any success?" he finally asks.

"Nothing so far. Or at least everything I've looked at has been snatched up already. Everyone seems to be buying. I can hardly get to talk to an agent even. But I've been busy with the minority arts report anyhow. We're setting up the steering committee."

"Who's chairing it?"

"That's one of the problems. We can't find the right person. Stuart Hall..."

"Who?"

"He's an academic at Birmingham, terrific – originally from Jamaica. He says he'll be on the committee but he hasn't the time to chair."

"You need someone with a name," he says firmly, "If you want people to take your report seriously. I could talk to Vic Feather of the TUC for you, or Dick Crossman. Both of them are keen on race."

"Mm... I'll talk to my committee."

My committee, my hand-picked committee – I am so proud of them, of us. As we troop into the bland boardroom of the Community Relations Commission – the sort of place more used to high-grade deliberations about quotas and immigration policy – we all have a sense of occasion, but we carry it lightly. We carefully don't look at each other as we spread ourselves around the polished table, jotters laid out in readiness for us, pens and glasses of water. It has been a battle – but a polite battle – to establish the principle that the advisory committee has to be made up of black and Asian artists. But we've won. Eight of us – actors like Norman Beaton and Taiwo Ajai, my old friend and ally musician Peter Blackman,

Ravi Jain who heads the National Association of Asian Youth and Shantu Meher who runs Leicester's Gujarati folk dance group, The Aryans. Last in has been artist Ossie Murray, and of course our long-distance member, Stuart Hall. All good people, tough people with experience and not a prima donna amongst them.

"Why do we need a chairman at all?" asks Peter. "We can manage very well without one."

But the three officers from the three organisations sponsoring our report – Arts Council and Gulbenkian Foundation as well as CRC – who sit in regular attendance shake their heads. Not the done thing at all. We've got to have a chair.

"Absolutely right," John agrees, when I relay the conversation to him later, "Even if it's just for the name. 'The Crossman Report' or the 'Whoever Report."

"But I thought it'd be my report."

"That won't get any notice."

The next time the committee meets however, the head of the Community Relations Commission, has a solution.

"Professor Hines, from Birkbeck University. Jamaican. Good chap. What do you think? We think he's very sound."

Everyone shifts. Peter shrugs.

"I vote we give the man a go," says Norman Beaton finally.

"We don't actually know him," Shantu Meher demurs.

"But it's true we need a figurehead," Ravi Jain, who's had more to do with bureaucracy than any of us, points out. We respect this, and nod.

"I feel like we're innocents in blunderland," I complain to Peter, when I climb the stairs to his roomy flat in West Hampstead a few days later.

"No, no," he shakes his head vigorously. "Don't let them intimidate you, not for even one moment! It's all just systems designed to keep us in our place. If we want to do things in our own way, we will. We don't like this Hines, we don't have to have him."

He strides across the room with his small-man's cocky walk, and slaps his coffee cup down on the top of a bongo that acts as a table.

This is what I need – Peter's abrasiveness and certainty and his cackle of a laugh.

"But our three officers are alright. In fact they've been pretty helpful."

"It's not individuals – that's the thing. It's the weight of the establishment. The old colonial mentality, the weight of history – that's what we're dealing with. Not individuals."

I look around the sitting room – it's well furnished with old comfortable sofas that look as if they've been used by generations of guests – the bright African fabrics, posters and musical instruments for Peter's group, Agor Mmba, his own large abstract paintings stacked up against one wall. I sigh. "Easy for you to say…"

He gives a deep guffaw, half bark of laughter, and pats me on the head. "Don't look so worried. We'll do alright. We know what we're doing."

And I believe him, even though it quickly becomes clear that we've taken on far more than the three funding bodies ever knew when they claimed this could be a quick part-time job.

The questionnaires have gone out to all local authorities that look relevant. But the information that's come back is alarmingly sparse. When I place it before my committee, I feel like a cat who's just brought in an exceedingly small mouse.

Norman fans the completed questionnaires out over the table and we all bend over them. They document such small, pathetic events – a few hundred pounds to a dance group here, permission for a carnival procession 'to process through the local park' there. No money – just permission. "Big deal."

Ravi picks up another and reads aloud, "'There are books in Eastern European and Asian languages in some of our libraries.'"

"That's really what you might call 'scraping the barrel'," says Norman.

We all know it's wrong. I think way back to the Indian Association of my childhood and their music and dance performances; to all the hidden societies we'd encountered when I was an Indian dancer and we took our company round Britain; to the black theatre groups and struggling centres that I'd talked to when I was at *Time Out*. Most of those don't show up in the replies that have come in from local authorities. Invisible.

It is depressing.

"You can't know what's going on by sitting in London," Peter declares. "You've got to get out there."

"Off to where?" asks John. I can hear exasperation seeping down the phone line. "You've only just come back."

"We're planning – Leeds certainly, Manchester… Oh, and Shantu thinks I ought to go and look at groups in Derby too…"

"You're running around far too much, I never get to see you."

"I'll be back in a week, or a bit more."

"I don't see why you have to actually go there anyway. They could just send you the information."

Ah, little does he know, I think but do not say.

CHAPTER THIRTEEN
1974

Nobody would choose Euston Station – grey, monochrome and functional Euston – for the start of a voyage of discovery. But being on the road with no idea of what lies ahead is deeply thrilling. Even the acrid smell of the concourse is exciting, even the few remnants of the IRA's bombing. Here I am, far too early for my train – Manchester isn't even signalled yet. I hang around the concourse, jostled by flurries of people who see their own trains announced and rush off platform-wards. Nobody looks at anybody or catches anyone's eye. No-one knows what I am up to. I am on a mission.

My suitcase is very light. Peter and Taiwo have given me some contacts and Norman's briefed me about his days at the Liverpool Everyman. I've packed cyclostyled sheets of official addresses for local authority offices (and I don't hope for much from them, on past record). But otherwise I'm flying blind. "Poor you," said John when he saw my itinerary, but poor nothing, I think. I can't think of anything I'd rather be doing.

My compartment's half empty and after Newark I've got it all to myself. The landscape races alongside us and the train clacks. We judder our way smartly north – 'dubbetty-dub, dubbetty-dub: electric-now, electric-now'. None of the grumbling lurches of the old steam trains. The engine occasionally just gives a deep kettle-like hiss.

Manchester and Bradford, Bristol and Leeds – all the towns and cities where migrants have come and settled. The clubs that seamen set up generations ago in Cardiff and Liverpool are on my list and the Midlands towns where Shantu stresses her fellow-Gujaratis have settled. "Call me regularly," John instructed.

"I'll try, but it could be difficult. You know it can be really hard to find a phone box. Or one that works."

"There'll be a phone in your hotel room surely."

Not so surely. I'm going to be staying in small B & Bs or with strangers who are friends of friends.

No hotels, no certainty. Footloose and open to the world.

"I'll try and find a phone box," I promise.

But by Wednesday, in Manchester, the thrill of the hunt has worn thin. I've gone from office to local authority office and I'm deadened by meetings and weighed down with reports about policies and programmes. I've heard about school figures, European funding programmes and library subventions but very little about culture.

I am starting to think that maybe I'll take the evening off. It's starting to rain and everyone else is going home to families and supper. But my cheap B & B near the station isn't a cheerful place to spend an evening in. So finally I find the bus to somewhere called Wilmslow where a Dr Desai has agreed to meet. He runs the local Indian Association, and that briefly stirs nostalgic memories of childhood for me. And there'll be some other people in the Gandhi Hall, he's promised, for me to interview as well. By now it's dark and raining hard and I can hardly see out of the windows of the bus. "Your stop, love," calls the driver. No-one else gets off. The streets are residential and deserted. Is this really Brunswick Road? Occasionally cars pass with a hiss as they hit puddles but the only other sound is amplified music thudding miserably out of a fake Tudor-style pub I squelch past.

I wonder if I'll miss the Gandhi Hall – maybe it'll be like the Dark and Light. But then there it is – a single-storey institutional building set back between well-appointed houses. A string of wet bunting is looped over the front in Indian colours. I go down the path and push the door open and immediately find myself in a large neon-lit hall. In the middle there's a group of young Indian men – all dressed as if they've come straight from the office – playing badminton. In a far corner there's a life-size statue of a god – at this distance I can't see which one – wreathed in twirls of incense. This isn't quite what I expected.

"Dr Desai?" I ask tentatively. One of the young men politely puts his racquet down and escorts me to a side office where I find half a dozen middle-aged men sitting and chatting. A small spare man detaches himself. This must be Dr Desai. "Come in," he instructs, "Take your coat off. Leave your umbrella – no, not there. Here. Please sit." I sit and drip. "I shall call for tea."

The others, he explains, are all members of the Management Committee, all waiting for me and eager to know how they can help. I sip hot tea and explain about the hunt for arts activities and events and they nod sagely – very important, culture. Culture and tradition. We are all in agreement.

This is the whole basis for the Gandhi Hall, they say. "A big achievement.

This is the first Indian centre in the whole of Manchester, you must know.."
It's only five years old, it used to belong to the Seventh Day Adventists,
and now is a resource for the city's entire Indian community. "You will
see!" They put in comments, one after the other stressing its access and
value.

"Everyone, it benefits everyone, our youth and our ladies who are very
much involved."

They all nod.

"And we support our own priest," puts in another proudly. "You'll have
seen the shrine in the corner of the hall?"

"And well supported!"

Dr Desai gets out a list. "We have five hundred members, but," he
wags a finger, "They are all heads of household. So in effect we have, if
we count families, well over two thousand members!"

"And very active support," rumbles another.

There are grunts of assent and they waggle their heads in that Indian
way signifying agreement.

There is something deeply familiar about all this – the men's expansive
yet formal way of talking, their way of relating. They occupy the space
with unspoken confidence. What does it remind me of? I wonder as I
scribble. Then I realise it's the old Indian Association and the men – also
all doctors – of my father's generation. It makes me feel as if I am ten
years-old again and sitting quietly while the elders discuss.

A woman puts her head tentatively around the door.

"Um... Dr Sahib these men playing badminton, can you ask them to
stop? We would like to set up."

"Yes, yes," says Desai. We continue to talk.

"How about your young people?" I ask. I sort of hope to hear about
rebellion, youth drama or rock groups.

"Let them speak for themselves," he says. Four teenagers are summoned
and they sit uneasily on the edge of their metal chairs.

"These are our junior members. Tell Mrs Khan," – I don't correct him
– "What your programme is."

They mutter sheepishly in turn – youth club, outings, sports – and
when they are allowed to go spring up with alacrity.

The woman reappears, flanked by a companion now, looking more
decisive.

"Can't they stop?"

I look covertly at my watch. I have been there an hour and I have
assembled what strike me as a pretty meagre set of facts.

"We really need to set up, Doctor Sahib."

"Is there an event?" I ask.

He looks surprised. "It's Navratri of course."

Navratri – the nine nights' festival – of course: how could I have not known?

Outside I can hear that more and more people are arriving and finally the plink-plonk of the badminton does cease.

"We need more chairs," says the woman, quite forceful now, and we stand up and are dispossessed. In the hall, young men are rolling a big carpet out to cover the space. Trestle tables and more chairs are being placed around the walls.

Cars are drawing up outside and families disgorge, crowding into the Gandhi Hall shedding wet coats and the woman emerging transformed with glittering gold jewellery and shot-silk Benarsi saris. Long elaborately teased hair is shaken out and there's a concerted dash towards the cloakroom.

The men have faded away and I find myself passed over to the organising women who are all busy and don't know who I am at all. They park me in one corner among the grannies. None of them speak English, but they smile at me broadly in a toothless manner and one of them pats my shoulder.

The room is getting warmer and noisier. The women return with much high chatter and laughter and the smell of incense mingles with the aroma of curry. A harmonium is tuning up reedily in a corner and after a time a few women tentatively start to sing. They sing a few phrases, stop and giggle, and then resume more confidently. Slowly others join in and soon the hall is resounding with voices singing together. Dancing starts, with two big circles, one inside the other. Everyone knows exactly what to do without being told; they go to their places. The women on the inside progress round the outer circle of males, stopping at each one in turn and then moving on. Clap-clap, turn, clap – move on. Saris swish and long plaits or teased hair swing, jewellery chinks in time to the music. It's bouncy and infectious and such fun. In my corner with the grannies my feet tap to the beat.

My grannies are swaying and clapping to the music. "Garba," says the one next to me who's tucked her feet underneath her and is sitting cross-legged on her chair. She points at the dancers and mimes approval. I do the same back.

Hours later I emerge into the quiet Manchester night where the lights of all the nearby houses have gone out and decent folk are all abed. My head is ringing with the music and the rhythm and the high happy energy of dancers and grannies and all. I am full of curry and am holding a small slightly sticky package of prasad in one hand.

Does this count as art, I wonder, back in my neat and neutral B & B. I am not sure. But it was fun. I snack on my prasad and can't be bothered to brush my teeth and fall asleep on my narrow bed.

When I wake, I find I am still thinking of Birmingham's old Indian Association. "There's a phone box down the hallway, honey," says the woman on the desk, "Just by the conveniences." I feed my money in and dial Acocks Green 3414. A voice answers and I press Button A; the money goes clattering into the box. It's Abba. I'm surprised. Shouldn't he be at surgery?

"Where have you been? Why don't you keep in touch? We've been trying to find you. Your mother's not very well.

"It's her chest again, the bronchitis," he says briefly. "I had to get her admitted to East Birmingham. I brought her home yesterday."

"I'll be there. I'll be with you in a couple of hours."

She's in bed and wheezing and her breathing sounds laboured. "I can leave you then," says Abba, and it's clear he is relieved. "I'll go and do my afternoon visits." Mother squeezes my hand conspiratorially. "I'm so glad you're here. Go and get me some cigarettes," she whispers.

I am shocked. "You must be crazy!"

She pulls her hand away petulantly.

"But why don't I remake your bed for you. You'll be more comfortable."

"No," she says restlessly. "I'm going to get up."

"Are you sure you should...?"

"I can't just lie here. I'm bored. There's nothing to do."

She comes down slowly in her red shiny dressing gown holding tightly onto the banisters, one step at a time like a child. I hover behind until she sits down at the table by the breakfast room window with a let-out breath.

"Look at the garden. So much to do and I can't do anything," she grumbles.

I start to tell her about my travels, and the events in Manchester, about how little I know of Britain. "I've never even been to Manchester..." I start to say.

"Oh, you have. You were too young and you don't remember. We used to drive up to Manchester to visit the Shahabs."

"And," she goes on, "Your father and I used to live there for a time before you were born."

"Really? Why?" This is news to me. But then I've never had too clear a picture of my parents' life before I arrived.

"That was long before they brought the National Health Service in. In those days, doctors had to buy their own surgery. And of course we weren't married long and we didn't have any money. So your father used to take on different locum jobs here and there so we could save for a surgery."

"How long were you there?"

"Oh, I don't remember. But have a look in there, in that big box." She waves a hand at the corner cupboard. "And you can make me a cup of tea while you're about it."

I take out a large cardboard box. It is filled with creased faded photographs. "Take them out." I tumble them onto the table.

"A cigarette would be nice with my tea..."

I ignore her. I am rifling among photos of their past – all black and white and full of people I don't know at all. And faded.

"Look at this one, Mum, you are wearing a *sari!*" Astounding.

She snorts.

"First time and last time! All his idea. You can see – he had no idea how to tie a sari. He just wound it round and round me like a parcel"

She's certainly right. The sari hangs in a very odd way. And she's also standing very stiffly, as if she doesn't dare move an inch. Abba on the other hand is perfectly at ease. He is standing proudly beside her in his usual three-piece suit with a kind of proprietorial glow.

"But you look so sweet... so shy."

She does. She is dark and doe-eyed and sort of dewy.

"That was before I came to my senses."

I pick up other pictures, a group of four young beaming men, Abba among them. "And who are these?" They are all wearing new greatcoats and slightly too large trilby hats as if was as some sort of merry masquerade. It's a jape – "Look at us playing at being English!"

Mother peers at it. "That's Dr Shahab. I don't remember the names of the others. Sarkar? Rizvi? There were so many. They were all students, when we were up in Manchester. That was when your father was doing his MBBS or was it LRCP...?"

There are more of the cheery men, sometimes with their arms daringly round the waists of young Englishwomen with 1930s marcelled hair and cheeky cloche hats. "And here's Abba! Who's he with?!"

"That was his landlady's daughter. That was before I met him. Look, here's one of him with her mother. They were very kind to your father. He was very fond of them both."

The mother is a sober-looking plump woman in a long dark dress with little round glasses.

"I heard they got killed in the war, with the bombing..."

I only half hear this. I lay out the pictures, piles of them. "Everyone looks so *happy*."

"We were..."

I can see her hand twitching automatically for a cigarette that's not there.

"We had no responsibilities. The others had all come from strict backgrounds in India. So this was freedom for them. They used to go out ballroom dancing and went to tea in Lyons Corner House and had girl friends. I remember they were always laughing."

"Ah..." She picks up a rather formal picture of a handsome young man, very serious looking – the sort of picture to send back to ones family. "That's Dr Farouq. Ah, I remember him, and Elsie. He was," and she smiles fondly, "So very much in love..."

She stops, and I wait. She is miles away.

"But then," she sighs deeply, "Then he got his degree and he had to go back to Beirut where his family had arranged his marriage with his cousin.

"He cried and cried on my shoulder," she said. "How he cried... Ah, poor man."

The ghost of the young doctor hovers over our breakfast table, and I wonder.

"How did you meet Abba?" I ask.

"Oh, quite by accident. When that man, Hitler got himself elected your grandfather sent me to England to learn English. He said 'Hitler's just a lightweight, a joke. He'll be gone in a year or two at most."

"He got that pretty wrong!"

"They all thought that then. So I signed up in a language school and I made friends with a Swiss girl called Gisela. She was going out with your father and she kept going on about 'Wasi this' and 'Wasi that'. 'He's so clever'. 'So exotic'. So finally I got fed up and said, 'I've got to meet this paragon!'

"And the great day came..."

She's sitting up straight now. Her colour is better and her eyes are sparkling.

"And the door opened, and then this... little man came..." and she pauses for effect, "Came *waddling* in. And I thought, ach, is *that* what all the fuss was about!"

"Well, and then," she looks wicked and smug, 'We started going out together,"

"Gisela must have been furious."

She snorts, "She stole my best suitcase. She was going back to Switzerland for a few weeks and asked if she could borrow it. And that was the last I saw of it!"

It strikes me Mother was the winner – a suitcase for a fully-fledged albeit 'exotic' doctor – but forty years on the loss of the suitcase still rankles.

There's the sound of a key turning in the front door. Abba's back and has finished his home visits.

He comes into the room and looks at her approvingly. "Good. You're looking much better, Gerda. Let me take your pulse...

"Just stop with those wretched cigarettes. They're the cause of all your problems... No, don't turn away..."

"You're always going on at me." She coughs defiantly. "I'm going to go and lie down for a bit."

He's abstracted when I get his morning coffee. He fiddles with his letter-opener, checks that the clock is keeping the right time. "Those cigarettes..." he says aloud. I get up. "Now where are you going?"

"I've got to get started getting supper together."

"No need to bother, I'm not hungry."

"There are other people."

But when I dish up the risotto, he tucks in.

"The old Indian Association – do you remember it? Does it still meet?" I ask. "I wouldn't mind talking to some of them."

"All gone. Broken up," says Mother, whom I've tempted downstairs. Of course, Abba doesn't like conversation at meals. "You know Dr Sethi died, didn't you?"

"Anthony's dad?"

"Heart attack. Just like that. And Dr Majmudar. And Dr Prem, he died in a traffic accident."

Nevertheless, I drive around nostalgically while Mother rests in the afternoons (and is probably hunting for cigarettes in old coat pockets). It looks as if everything is crumbling, not just the Indian Association. The old monuments I'd thought were so solid and fixed have turned shabby and apologetic. The Good Companions, the mega pub across the main Coventry Road, always had a sort of brutal glamour, a bastion I knew I'd never enter. But now it looks seedy and appears barely used.

"And the Tivoli's gone," I report, when I get back from another foray. Mother looks puzzled, "You know, the big cinema on the Coventry Road."

"Oh that. That went long ago."

And Ffulkes Furriers up at Five Ways where Abba took me to see his brand of India is lost somewhere, like a mafia victim, under a ferocious series of concrete overpasses and underpasses that people are calling Spaghetti Junction.

"And the Bullring," Mother says. "You remember I used to take you to the market there when you were little?"

"They sold rabbits."

"They sold everything, not just rabbits. Fresh produce and plants. And when we kept chickens, that's where I used to get my chicks. It's all concrete now."

Discount shopping centres, dual carriageways, massive sodium lights – it's hard to feel affection for this place or a connection with it.

"And there's another one going," I point out to Mother when I drive her to Moseley Village to the cake shop she fancies. Another monstrous cinema – "'Dreamlands' – what a name!" – is festooned with tacky posters for Hindi movies and... I slow down.

'Mushaira' it says. A mushaira in Dreamlands? How odd, how unlikely. I've never been to a mushaira...

"You're surely not planning to go? To that sort of place?" Mother sometimes knows me too well.

"Well," I say judiciously, 'It would be work...'

"Ach!" she says in a German explosion of disgust. "I give up!"

But when I drive back to Balsall Heath later that evening, I do wonder if she mightn't be right. It's a daft idea. For a start the cinema is vast. It's one of those old dinosaurs where once people turned out in their hordes on a Saturday night to see Bette Davis and Cary Grant. It's huge and it's dilapidated – hardly the sort of place to stage a poetry evening.

They've probably got a side room. But then, whoever heard of a cinema with a side room?

At night time the place is different though. It's garlanded with lights now. It has cars turning in and parking in the dusty forecourt. It is still distinctly *gundi*, but now it's a friendly *gundi*. And a popular *gundi*. The inhabitants of Balsall Heath, Sparkbrook, Sparkhill – all those areas that Abba pointedly avoided when I drove round with him on his doctor's visits all seem to be flocking into Dreamlands. I manoeuvre Mother's car into a tight space and then I hover by my car door. The crowd is mainly male; I feel and look out of place.

140

'Madam?' a young man with a clipboard approaches. I am a journalist, I explain. Before I can say much more, I am being pulled through the crowd – "I am Salman," he calls, "I'm one of the organisers... Please come this way," – through to a place at the front of a half-empty gallery, looking down onto the busy melee below.

It is all most odd. This is not what I expect a poetry reading to be, and I do wonder if I have not made the most ghastly mistake. Maybe I am here for a Hindi movie, a special preview perhaps? Masses surely can't turn out like this for *poetry*?

I wait confidently for a screen to be lowered, but instead a line of people walk in a slightly unplanned sort of way onto the bare stage. There's a buzz of expectation in the audience. Another young man – as discreet and dapper as Salman 1 – brings on a standing microphone. The people, fifteen men and two women, look at each other uncertainly and then follow the lead of the first – a thick-set man in an astrakhan cap – and sit down cross-legged on the floor. Salman 3 comes in and hands out tins of Pepsi-Cola to each in turn. The lights in the auditorium are finally switched off.

I blink at what follows...

One after another, each person gets up and goes to the microphone. There's no fuss or flummery. No great drama. Some of them bring out sheets of paper and read their verses. Some know them by heart. Many of them intone and chant, and the rhythm is intoxicating. The audience sways with it. They know that each verse takes the complex imagery on a few steps. The poets build and embellish, and invite us to join and follow the intricacy. Occasionally one of them will pause and savour the moment and let the audience taste the quality of his concept too. We love it. The resolution dangles, it entices: but when it does emerge, the sheer subtle cleverness of it is like the release of flood water and is greeted by gasps and cheers and heartfelt shouts of 'Wa!... Wa!'

This is more than enchanting. I grip the front of the balcony, spellbound. What do I know of Urdu, its conceits and the refined nature of Persianised verse? Fuck all. But I have had years of sitting in darkened auditoria as a theatre critic. I know authenticity. I know true passion. Fakery, melodrama, flabbyness – I can spot them in a trice, and I know they're not here tonight in Dreamlands.

In a pause, one of the Salmans nips up to the balcony with a warm can of Pepsi.

"It's amazing! Who are they all?"

"Mostly local. People who write poetry in their spare time. But then we had a real stroke of luck. We heard that Hafiz Jullundari – you've heard of him?"

I shake my head.

"He was actually due to visit family members here in Birmingham. What luck! He graciously agreed to appear. Back in Pakistan he's a complete star," he explained. "People will travel miles to hear him."

"And you, are you a poet?"

He looks bashful.

"Oh no, I'm a student. There's several of us – we got together because we all love Urdu poetry. Then some local Pakistani businessmen stepped in and offered us support – they believe the new generation don't know anything about their own culture. They've been really very supportive. When we suggested that they bring in three more poets, they agreed. The third man who recited, you remember him? The man in the sheepskin cap? That was Ahmad Faraz and Jamaluddin Ali came after him – they've both come specially from Pakistan, and then there was Qatil Shafai who's come from Paris."

"That must have been really expensive?"

"Oh, it was! In the region of £1,500. But we reckon there's around five hundred people here. Of course we've given out a lot of free passes. But still we hope to cover our costs."

"Maybe you could apply for a grant to the local arts council?"

He looks sceptical but is too well brought up, in a Pakistani way, to let himself show disbelief.

I take tales of the mushaira back to my committee in London. It's not easy, but I try, in the Community Relations Council's tasteful conference room, to recreate it. The humbleness, lack of pretension, the smell of old dust and left-over glory days: and the exhilaration. "Hm." Taiwo listens carefully. "It sounds rather like a ritual. Something bonding and private."

"Not at all!" Peter exclaims hotly. "It's shameful. All that quality pushed into a corner. Would we accept that?! Things like that, they should be right there in the mainstream. Where's the respect in being in an old cinema?"

"But why does it have to be respect on other's terms?" asks Taiwo acutely. The argument rolls on and we don't agree.

Wherever I've gone, I've encountered artists – dance groups or poets or painters or musicians – of every ethnicity and nationality. The country's full of unsuspected artists and almost all operating under the radar. It's different from our *Hustler* battles. They were robust battles over discrimination and inequality and disempowerment. Bad housing, harassment. If

I listen now – and it's really not so hard – I can hear all sorts of other things: stories of loss and pride and homelessness and making a home and courage and change...

Somewhere at the back of my mind I hear an echo – a bland new university high in the hills way above a misty distant Canterbury. A voice calling for the primacy of imagination... The ghost of Wilson Harris.

"Of course Peter's right. But it's not just about justice, is it? Not only..." I say.

An uproar.

"Listen to this," says Norman, "The report from Equity – only nineteen roles for black actors out of 1,296 roles in repertory theatres last year. And note this, 'Repertory theatre has already been described as the postgraduate field of training, but it would appear to be *closed.*'" He stops and emphasises, "'Closed', you note, to Afro-Asian artists."

He hits the desk. "Equality. Justice. I rest my case."

Another train, Derby next stop and I sit, reading Equity's report again. It is, in its own word, 'devastating', even worse than Norman said. There were nineteen theatre roles for black actors last year – but ten of them had been in just a single season of Athol Fugard's plays in Sheffield.

Now what to make of Derby? I can't think why I've chosen to go there. Neither Norman nor Taiwo have acted there. Peter's music group hasn't played there. 'Ukrainians' notes the brief data from the CRC. But the national Ukrainian Association didn't sound enthusiastic when I asked them about Derby. "A small community – only about three hundred. We consider it," they say, "Promising." Seems Derby is small beer compared with bigger centres with fully-functioning Ukrainian theatres and cultural centres, and I feel sympathetic to them as underdogs. But still, they're better dogs than Grimsby where the association records the presence of a mere twenty Ukrainians.

The address takes me to a comfortable-looking Victorian house set in a quiet Derby backwater. It looks sleepy and inside, in the extension tucked at the back, there are just nine youngsters warming up for dance rehearsals.

Their coach, a modest man in his 30s, opens his hands. "Derby County is playing Real Madrid this evening..." He shrugs resignedly. "But we can still show you something. We're taking part in a show to raise money for the Red Cross at the weekend. We're going to go over our items this evening."

He claps his hands, "Right, everyone. Back in your places. We'll do the Hopak." The youngsters who'd sat down lever themselves up and get back into formation. "This is very traditional," he tells me, sotto voce. "It comes from the area round Kiev." He sets the tape recorder going. There's a whirr while the dancers wait poised for the music to start.

It's catchy music, swinging bouncing accordion music. I push my chair back against the wall. A few feet away, the young dancers stomp and whirl in their high scarlet boots. I can hear them panting as they clap and the men swing their partners round. The floor vibrates and my hair lifts with the breeze they are making. Next three young women come to the fore and start to turn and turn in a dizzying series of fouettes. Round and round as if they'll never stop. On the sidelines the young men whoop encouragement. Maybe "Go for it!" in Ukrainian.

To one side of the dancing floor there's a small bar where a few thick-set old men are sitting with their beer and cards. They are watching the dancers from beneath bushy eyebrows in between each move in their game. I watch them watching covertly and wonder what they're thinking. They say little but I bet they are missing nothing.

Now the young men are stepping forward, easing the women aside and the tempo quickens even more. With a kind of fake nonchalance they embark on a series of amazing leaps, kicks and Cossack-type crouches. It's really flashy stuff. Impressive. I catch the old men's eyes, I mime 'wonderful'. They grunt something in Ukrainian. "What?" I ask the coach. He smiles.

"They said 'Child's play'," he translates. The men rumble on. "They say, when they were young, they could do much more than that. Much stronger. More leaps, more..." he casts his eyes affectionately up at the ceiling, "More virile."

The men nod and growl behind their heavy tobacco-stained moustaches. More Ukrainian comments.

"They are saying the younger generation don't understand the culture. Not any more."

The music comes to a wheezy stop and the young people break, collapsing round the bar, reaching for cold drinks. They're flushed and shining with effort but energised. "Don't forget to be here by 1 o'clock sharp on Saturday," the coach reminds them. And remember to iron their costumes, polish their knee-high boots, bring a packed lunch, he goes on. They nod politely. It is the usual routine.

"£25 for boots!" a fair-haired young woman with a pixie face tells me in a Midlands voice. "Czyprunka is going to ruin me." It does seem a lot. I do a quick mental sum. Multiply that by eighteen for the whole troupe (the missing football fans) and that comes to £450 on boots alone.

"You could apply to the local arts council for a small grant." I suggest.
"Oh no, we couldn't apply," says the coach firmly. "We're not English."
One of the old men growls something.
"He says, 'It is beneath our dignity to go to the assistance board'..."
"But you pay rates and taxes..."
They shake their shaggy heads.

The coach is gallant and insists on giving me a lift back to the station – "It might be rather noisy after the big match" – even though it's out of his way. I gather up my handbag and coat.

"Do you have trouble recruiting dancers?" I ask as we settle ourselves in his aged car.

"There's no problem. They're very keen. Everyone wants to keep hold of the culture. In fact," he changes gear, "You can say, with two dance groups, an orchestra and a choir, there must be, on average, a dancer or a musician in every Ukrainian family here in Derby!"

"Not English." I write in my notebook on the train and underline it again and again. It's not new. I've heard it so many times in all my journeying. And always in the same tone – courteous almost apologetic, but quite firm, as if it is an immovable barrier. They're born here, or came here as infants. They take their dances and songs and choirs to raise money for a huge amount of 'English' charities. But they still think of themselves as foreigners. So when does an art form become 'English'? Or when does a person become 'English'?

Way back, in Birmingham suburbs, I didn't have any doubts. I slipped like a fish through English waters. But it's a good question – who or what is English? Am I English? Strictly speaking, I'm British. But if I'm not proper English, I'm not proper German either. And my two years in Delhi showed me that I didn't feel at home in that visceral way there too. I wasn't proper Indian either.

It's a tricky thing, identity. I think back to all the times, from childhood up, when I've clearly bothered people because they couldn't place me – "How did you get your name?" And when I explain, "How interesting..." And then, insistently, "But *which side* do you identify with?" But maybe in these new times we need to rethink the idea of purity. Being British surely has to take in all the variations that I am unearthing, even if people seem shy to make that claim.

Liverpool, Cardiff, Leicester, Bristol, on and on, and time's passing. I talk to big-bearded Greek Orthodox priests, Chinese musical instrument-makers, Polish dramaturges, Caribbean painters, men in the old seamen's

Ibo Club and Yoruba Club, people struggling to establish black centres. I ask the larger-than life Louise Bennett – Miss Lou – about writing in patois. I visit Mas camps, when a hundred sewing machines in Notting Hill are whirring, turning out full-blown, sharp-edged costume fantasies – reams of them – for the annual street Carnival, a few years old and now getting into its fierce and wonderful stride. British, surely – shaped by the experience of living here?

But where's the recognition for all this? Why is it all so hidden? Which side does it identify with?

"Apply for grants?" ask black artists who give the impression of knowing the way the wind blows better than most. "Don't ever trust the council..." They say. I hear echoes of the Grove and its canny watchful survivors. £1,000 for a whole season of black plays, I think, for the Dark and Light, and a hassle.

I can't get invisibility out of my mind. Strange that an experience from childhood has had such a lasting effect...

I am ten years old again and sitting in the back of Abba's Citroen. We are leaving St Joseph's Primary or Nechells Secondary Modern or wherever it happened to be that month. Abba and Amma are chatting quietly in the front while I sit on the soft-smelling leather in the back. It's the end of a vivid talk-filled afternoon with the Indian Association. There've been singers and a short film about the moves for Indian Independence, and the men have talked politics and the women have gathered and gossiped and served out food. It's been warm and noisy and full of laughter, and I am happy and tired. As we leave I look out of the back window at the out-of-hours school, wanting to hang on to the feel of the event.

It is twilight now and the street lights are coming on. No-one's around. The gates to the school have been locked behind us and the playground is deserted. It is so empty. A sudden sense overwhelms me – we don't exist. There are no Indians anywhere else that I can see in Birmingham, just here on these hidden Sundays. When the teacher sweeps the big rubber across the blackboard at school, everything vanishes. There is just the blackboard. Just like that. As if we – and now more than we – were never there.

It is not, I think now, acceptable any longer.

CHAPTER FOURTEEN
1976

The big pine table in my front room has almost vanished under piles and piles of paper. Notes and interviews, figures and reports, sheets of carbon paper, packs of chalky white paper strips so I can correct all my typing mistakes (frequent). There's no space for my portable typewriter so I've parked it on the floor. And now there are estate agents' details too to add to the whole melee. I've got to sort it out. This is hopeless.

What a relief when Moira knocks at my door. Good, I can break off. But she bursts in and can hardly get a word out for agitation.

"Didn't you hear it? Last night?"

"No, I was over at John's. Not downstairs again?" I guess. "Billy and Stacey?"

She brushes aside my offer of coffee without really taking it in.

"I can't stand it any longer."

"But what on earth happened?"

She finally sits down but I can see she is still shaking. This is so unlike Moira, normally so controlled in a neat Scottish way.

"Well," she slowly regains her composure. "It was really late and someone rang my doorbell. I shouldn't have, but I went downstairs and there were three strangers, big men, all looking for Billy. Of course I wouldn't let them in. I had to shut the door in their face."

"Gosh."

"But they must have come back later and somehow got in. I could hear shouting and threats. It was awful. I very nearly called the police."

"You should have!"

"I was scared of Billy. What he might do to me."

"Should we tell the landlords?"

"Landlords – you're joking. What have they ever done for us?"

There is no doubt that our comfortable old house is falling about our ears. But a few days later fate takes a hand.

A letter arrives – one for me, one for Moira – from a Mrs Warren who says she is now the owner of 70 Ledbury Road. We have been sold, all of us, without our ever knowing we were up for sale in the first place. What's going to happen? We wait. Mrs Warren doesn't appear. Weeks go by. Even Billy and Stacey go quiet.

"Perhaps she won't appear?" Maybe it'll be just as it was, with us paying our rent once a week and being left to ourselves. £5 a week for the past ten years.

Moira who is much more canny than me doesn't believe it. She studies Mrs Warren's letter: on the surface friendly, but – she points out – very careful not to commit herself. "It reads as if she's shown it to a lawyer," she comments. Charles on the ground floor emerges for once – a rare sight – and says he he'd noticed men with clipboards studying our house and taking notes.

"Maybe she's going to do it up?"

Nobody thinks this is worth responding to. Notting Hill just isn't the sort of place that people do up.

Then one day, Billy and Stacy are no more. Gone. Just like that. What next? The silence is spooky. "I do not believe she is a benevolent woman," says Moira sombrely.

I'm home early one evening when I hear a rattle from the stairwell outside Moira's flat. It goes on for a time, and finally I put down my pad and go to see what she's up to.

But it's not Moira. It's a large homely-looking West Indian in his late thirties, in a dark knitted cap and donkey jacket. He's put a number of paint pots down on the stairs beside him and is busily trying to open her front door.

"Who are you?"

"Damn keys won't turn," he says crossly, looking down at the keys in his big hand. "Just don't seem to work."

"What are you doing?"

"I'm moving in." he says, "Or I would be if I could just get the door open. Do you live down there? We're going to be neighbours. I'm..."

"But you can't! Someone's living there."

"No, they've left. I'm moving in, once I've done it up." He gestures the paint pots. "They said it might need a bit of redecorating."

"Who said?"

"The people who let it to me, of course."

He has an honest sensible-looking face and doesn't look like my idea of a burglar, and too straightforward to be a con-man.

"My name's Sailor," he puts the keys down and holds out his large hand.

When Moira comes home, she finds Sailor and me drinking coffee and chatting and the way to her flat blocked by pots of Ultra White.

"I was talking to a man in the pub," Sailor explains again for Moira's benefit, "And I mentioned I needed a place to live. Seems he was managing a flat that had just got vacant. I could have it there and then, he said and it'd save him the trouble of advertising. And I'd get it cheap if I redecorated. Well you don't turn something like that down, do you? So I went and borrowed money for the deposit from my cousin down the way and then I got these keys."

He passes them over to Moira. "I never tried the front-door key – someone was just coming out and let me in, but this one here doesn't work."

"They're not the same as mine. Nothing like them," she says with relief.

"Ah, I guess I've been done," he says with a sigh, and shakes his head.

"Can you go and find the man you spoke to?"

"I'll go back to the pub and see if anyone knows him. But I'll tell you one thing for sure – I'll never see my money again. It's a wicked world." He puts his mug down and levers himself with some difficulty out of my low chair. He shrugs his big shoulders into his donkey jacket. "Well, thank you, ladies, for the coffee." He shakes our hands – "Pleasure to meet you," – and goes off into the night with his paint pots and we never see him again.

"Nice man," we say sadly to each other as I wash up the coffee cups. "Shame..."

John isn't nearly so sanguine. "Nice man? Balls! Get those estate agents details. I'll drive you round and you can look at new places."

I sigh.

"I dunno. I'm really not sure."

But the next day the police come round. They want to know what Moira and I know about Billy, where he is.

"When are you free?" I ask John.

It's not a hopeful trip. We drive around in his small MG but everywhere people seem to be on the move, and options disappear almost as soon as they're announced. We seem to travel with the constant background sound of building work. Hammering and drilling, demolition and reconstruction, new extensions going up, skylights, dormer windows going in. We dawdle fuming behind lumbering cement mixers that look as if they are on the way to the very properties that we are off to inspect.

"They're just flying off the page," the sleek estate agent announces.

"But here's one you might like to look at. It's just come in. But," he adds, "You'd better be quick."

Number 86 Grafton Road is a shambles, but at least it's an available shambles: nobody seems rushing to grab it and at £13,500 I could afford it. I approve of the road it's in: Grafton Road runs parallel to Kentish Town High Street and has a modest workmanlike feel to it, quite unlike the other side of the High Street that has 'come up' in the world. Junior politicians and media people live on the other side of the road, John tells me, but this side has no such aspirations. John purses his lips but I like places that haven't come up. The house itself is a Victorian terrace and has good lines if you look beyond the dilapidation. And it has a past too – at one time in its life, it was a fish and chip shop. A fish and chip shop! When I was a child I thought it would be heaven to actually live in a fish and chip shop. And here I am, in one at last.

It is definitely not habitable – floor-boards are up, the stairs have holes in them and are dangerous. Squatters who have moved on by now (even squatters reject it) didn't treat it well. But, "It's a good investment," says Abba. At this stage I think he'd feel a shoebox was a good investment.

"Kentish Town will come up," says John. And I sign on the dotted line. Now to find builders.

Not so easy. I never thought London could have so many. But they won't agree even to look at No.86. "Work on your property? Don't make me laugh, lady... Come back after Easter. Or maybe summer." I am the owner of a wreck, and I think I'll never be able to move in. Then I stumble on the Gentle Ghosts who operate on the margins. I find Jim who is a drop-out architect and says he can see possibilities, and his partner, Sandy who's a qualified builder. The three of us spend hours with plans and bits of paper and slowly the place confirms that, yes, it does have possibilities. We dream up an en suite bathroom in a little attic where I can lie in the bath and look over the rooftops of Kentish Town; we rescue the old green and white fish-and-chip shop tiles still remaining in the lobby.

I suggest a pond in the living room on the first floor but Jim shows an unexpected streak of caution and says he thinks it could be too heavy for the floor. We do have fun, even without a pond. But it does take an awful lot of time – months in fact since Sandy and Jim and the Gentle Ghosts vanish whenever there's a solstice. I finally meet the invisible Mrs Warren who is delighted to see me go, and I move into the top floor of Grafton Road. Most days I pick my way round building debris, but too often debris with an absence of builders. Where are they? When will they return to finish the work? I wonder if it's dust that's making me retch or if it's stress over lack of progress. How much longer?

"We all feel you're spreading bad vibes," the Ghosts say sternly when they get back from the Isle of Wight,

"We think it would be better if you moved out. Why don't you go and stay with John for a while?"

But I have my own deadline, apart from the need to pull the ethnic arts report together.

It's not the dust or the invisible Ghosts that's making me retch. Who would have thought it? It is becoming clear beyond any doubt that I am pregnant.

* * *

It feels so good to be back in the Grove. We are hemmed in by crowds and nearly deafened by the boom-boom-thud of music and shrill high whistles from dancers who are somewhere over there but I'm not quite sure where because I can't see much over the heads of all the people.

"Look!"

"Where?"

"Over there – coming round the corner."

"I'll take Amelia," and John grabs the child who takes this all cheerfully in her eight-month stride.

Bright jazzy wings of costumes appear tacking jerkily to and fro over the bobbing dancing crowd. They look like shark's fins.

"I think it's Sukanya," I shout. I have to shout because there's another float approaching from another direction with the thump of its conflicting rhythms and the yells of supporters running beside the lorry drown me out. "They're playing African tribes…"

"What tribes?"

"African!" I bellow

Amelia thinks this is all lovely – the shouting and the banging and the steady drumming rhythm. She jumps up and down in John's arms and then tries to pull his hair. We have struck gold with this child. She's arrived with enthusiasm for everything on offer.

"This way. Come over this way," shouts John, and I tag after him as we work our way along the pavement past a large woman in a baseball cap who's selling homemade patties from a table at the foot of her steps and sweating in the heat. The smells and the smoke of everywhere is overwhelming– hot fat and frying and charcoal, and something, I sniff, I bet it's weed. Of course, it would be. What else? This is the Grove.

Further on there's a heavyset Rasta with a large knitted cap who's got a big tub with ice and bottles of Fanta. Lovely. And a little way on there's a brazier and blackened corn on the cob the way they do it in India. We push our way between heaving crowds swaying and jumping to the heavy beat. A very old man – definitely high on something – comes dancing by in his own private world. "Bless you, little baby!" he declares as he comes up to us and kisses Amelia's bare toes and then is lost again in the melee.

Who would have thought the Grove, our old Grove, could be so transformed? Carnival has burst all over it like a juicy fruit. Every house door is opened. People spill out onto all the steps, climb on the railings for a better view.

"Is there a programme?" shouts John. "Or a route?" And of course there isn't. The floats and the flatbed lorries are going wherever they want to or wherever they see an opening. We have to hunt them, following the raw sound and the flash of gauze and the skirling whistles. The air is strident with sound systems from one street, reggae from another. There is no order, none at all, and that is fine. We just manage to cross the road before a large phalanx of multi-coloured insects, their wings high and shiny, comes bearing down. They are sashaying together in a syncopated beat – stamp, shuffle, sway, stamp, shuffle, sway – and have the abstracted distant look of people in an ecstatic dream. The Queen in their midst comes regally by, her vast billowing costume cunningly supported on concealed wheels. Acres of spangles, miles and miles of wire. It is dazzling and wondrous.

"There's something happening on Ladbroke Grove!" The rasping sound of a brass band comes growling raucously over. We push and shove past old landmarks. This is where Courtney lived. And there's Mrs Laslett's place. What is she making of the way her small Carnival has taken root? It's turned into such a wild blossom of un-Englishness. We fight and push our way along the old streets and they cease to be the places of bitterness and struggle and deprivation that they were in the *Hustler* days. It is one big glorious noisy party.

A big band of matrons from the Dominican Association come round the corner, processing in their national costume, ample hips swinging, liming in stately unison. I blink. "Hey! Isn't that the receptionist in our health centre?" She still looks stern behind her horn-rimmed specs, as stern as you can be in this frenzied ambiance. Now I know about her secret life I will never be scared of her again. But then I look again and it's a lookalike. Or maybe not, who knows...?

We get borne along Ladbroke Grove heading north – could that be

Raju, I wonder, leaning against the struts of the structure for another sound system? But too late, we are past and he is lost. But when we get to the big overpass someone else hails me. It is the epic poet who'd been such a trouble in *The Hustler*. "Come and see our exhibition!" he shouts. "It's brilliant!" He is ebullient. He's forgotten I cut his verse, or maybe it just doesn't matter any more. "We'll come back later," I shout back but I don't think he heard me. Somewhere in the throng I know that Peter is here with Lord Eric and his band and Marvin. And Leslie Palmer who's masterminded all this. Should I be taking notes for the report, I wonder for a brief moment. But I met and talked to Leslie – slim, sharp and handsome – a few days ago and he was dizzy with fatigue even then. What magic. When I still lived in the Grove, Carnival was just a little random thing. Now Leslie has inspired, enthused and sweet-talked just about everybody he knows – bands and youths and stall-holders and calypsonians and West Indians from every island, big and small. And the upshot is this – not a kindly fete as it had been, but an extravaganza, with a new raw exultant edge.

A group of skeletons pass, big drums banging. They wear fixed painted-on mocking grins. Bones and death.

This is different. It's not the secret hidden activities of the Indians I met in the Gandhi Hall, or the red-booted Ukrainians. This is out on the street. "It's resistance," says Peter happily when we meet up at our next committee meeting. "It's 'our ting.'"

"Not my ting," says Norman as he lowered himself onto the low chair with a clear groan of a man with a large hangover. "This is a Trinidad 'ting.'"

"Oh ho, not fancy enough for you, eh? Mr Shakespeare man?"

"Gilbert and Sullivan now, actually," he says stiffly. "And don't you rile me, my man. My credentials are solid."

We know that. Peter is just fooling. We all know that Norman is a superb actor. He triumphed in Jonathan Miller's 'Tempest' and now he's reaping great notices in the West End in 'The Black Mikado'.

"I was really shocked." I look for my notes. "That whole Carnival, do you know what the budget was? Leslie Palmer had something like £3,000 to do it! That was for both days in Notting Hill, and for the dance the night before in the Hammersmith Palais too."

Actually none of us are really surprised. The way the report is turning out, it's clear that the groups I've been talking to have all been existing on handouts and peanuts.

"Sorry, it's not £3,000," I check my notes again. "It's more, it's £3,755."

153

Peter snorts. "And just look at what he lined up – at least a dozen steel-bands, and I don't know how many mas groups and dancers. Bloody amazing!"

"'I've got six mas groups down in my notes. But I'm sure we saw more on the day.'"

"People just join in of their own accord," Peter says. "Black people are spontaneous. We don't need everything to be all pre-planned and programmed."

This is a bit much. Romantic, or what?

"Come on, Peter! You've got to have planning,' Taiwo protests. "Leslie didn't even know about some of the grants till just a few weeks before the day!"

"OK, OK." He surrenders.

"And no help either," I go on, "He said the Council wouldn't close the streets, wouldn't even provide toilets."

Everyone has stories of parsimony – and worse. Shantu's dance group couldn't afford hall rental in Leicester, so now they rehearse in her backyard. "And I paid for their costumes," she adds in her soft voice. "A hundred pounds is a lot out of my youth worker's salary."

"Ask Frank Cousins. Now he could tell you some stories," Norman interjects. "He's not a weak man but..."

Ah, I remember Frank Cousins and my visits down to the Dark and Light in the Longfield Hall.

"Fighting the Arts Council nearly destroyed him."

"They put everything we do under the heading 'community arts,'" mutters Ravi. "Even Indian classical music."

"'Community arts' – glorified social work." Norman is scornful. "No respect. Alfred Fagon's got it. Listen to this. This is what he says in his new play." He clears his throat and then drops into easy Jamaican: "Don't depend on the Council for anything. The only help the council give black people for their art is an old church hall in Brixton called the Dark and Light Theatre, and another at King's Cross called the Keskidee. Never go and watch black people's works of art. The buildings are so old that if the draught don't kill you, the building will collapse and kill you instead!"

We laugh but it is rueful.

"Containment, that's what it's about," says Peter firmly. "You saw all those lines of police at Carnival? It's to pen us in."

But the work of all kinds that we are documenting can't be penned in. It is too big and too noisy. We're reaching the end of our task, and we study the score-sheet. The hidden art that we've turned up is immense.

Existing with little evidence in general sight are dance groups, theatre groups, choirs, orchestras, writers, publishers, painters, poets. National festivals for Bhangra and Ukrainian dance and Steel Band. Chinese Full Moon and dragon-dancing for the New Year.

I collect up figures and do a sum. "If I add up all the amounts that local authorities across the country have given to what they call 'minority arts', it comes to £4,254." What a joke. Some councils get back and say they don't have figures because they "don't believe in separating people out".

"Sounds good," says Peter, "But actually, discrimination by neglect."

I write the report that describes it. "And now what?" Taiwo leans forward.

"Recommendations," Ravi joins in. "It's no good protesting. What do we want to change?"

We all argue for some time. How do we frame them? It's easy to say what we want. We want to stop being exotic or invisible. We want to stop being 'community arts' (unless we are). We want knowledge about who we are, information, avenues out of ghettoes, and respect. Equality, lack of discrimination. We want to be who we are.

"That's OK, but please tell me how do I boil all that down in recommendations?"

Our minders from our funding bodies step in. They are official arts people and they know the terrain and which levers to press. Think of all the official avenues that need to open out and integrate, they prompt – think of cultural bodies, umbrella bodies, government departments, training organisations, museums and galleries, the BBC.

The BBC... Hmm. We eye each other across the conference table and I'm certain we're all remembering the day the man from the BBC came to give evidence – a plump self-satisfied man who clearly thought we were making a fuss about nothing. "The BBC is conscious of its responsibilities to society, and of its wish never to leave behind, in any programme – fact or fiction – a sediment that could be construed as likely to exacerbate racial tension in any form." It all comes down, he said, to quality alone. Race had nothing to do with it.

"Jolly good," muttered Norman under his breath in his best Colonel Blimp impersonation. "Top hole."

And then it comes down to a title for our report. We decide to get back to it later.

The summer comes and a stroke of luck. Old friends of John have been renting a little house on a tidal island off the Essex coast. It's a tiny pocket-handkerchief of an island, just a set of fields, no more, with a small cluster of wooden clapboard houses. Would we like to use their house occasionally over the next few months?

Because it's tidal, we have to wait for the sea to turn. Once that happens, an ancient pock-marked track snakes up from the muddy seabed. It is edged with big boulders that are festooned with seaweed. We sit waiting and watching from the top of the rise. Is it really clear all through? The tide goes down in little bits and some of the track is still in deep water. Once it's clear, we bump over its uneven surface painfully slowly, steering round deep pools of water full of life left by the receding tide, mussel shells and bladderwrack. It smells pungent and very old. The Danes would have smelt the same odour when they charged over the causeway to massacre the Brits a thousand years ago.

I've packed up my papers and closed down my typewriter. I am going to forget about culture and about race for a few days. I'm going to a place that has been scrubbed clean of present history. Seabirds, the occasional rusty sail of an Essex barge puffing by. Space. Emptiness.

We drive through the East End and out by Ilford where John grew up. We've done it before and every time he points out the street where he lived and the school bus stop and where he used to pedal his bicycle after his sign-writer father. I know it all by heart now and its post-war bleakness reminds me comfortably of the Birmingham suburb where I grew up and Rowlands Road.

This time it's getting late because the tide has not been co-operative.

"Let's stop and get some fish and chips," John says. "Pull over here. I know this place. It's where we used to go..."

"Great – I love fish and chips."

It's a standard corner shop in a small line of local shops, windows slightly steamed up from the huge metal containers filled with hot oil and sizzling fish. It's busy when we get in. A group of black teenagers, all loud and mouthy, are in possession and are shouting across at each other and teasing each other in broad West Indian. I push in towards the counter. No-one stands aside, not because they are hostile but because their young thing is just much more important. But then I notice John.

John is as white as a sheet.

"Let's go," he says tersely.

"But..."

"Come on. We're not wanted here."

He has headed back to the car without waiting for me. The traffic on the road out of London holds me back on the pavement. When I finally reach the car he is in the passenger seat shaking.

"Fuck, fuck, fuck.." he is saying intensely and he bangs the dashboard with his fist time after time.

"What can..."

"Nothing. Nothing!" he shouts again, this time loudly. "Let's go."

I put the car into gear and wait for a break in the traffic. It takes an age, or it feels like an age. Big pantechnicons and heavy lorries go thundering past and our little Ford Fiesta sits and judders in their slipstream. I don't know what to do. I am shocked by violence of his reaction. But his memories and his home turf, I recognise, have been wrenched away from him. It must feel like a violation.

Britain is changing and we are part of the change. And people will get damaged or feel damaged in the process and territory will be challenged and lost. I can't tidy that away with accounts of cultural delight and harmony.

But nevertheless, I don't tell the others about the incident when we meet back again. We are in the Gulbenkian's Regency Terrace office this time, a stone's throw from Regents Park.

"So what are we going to call it? Who can think of a name?"

Everybody looks down studiously at their notepads. Shantu shifts in her seat. Peter sighs loudly. But it's no good, we've got to bite the bullet. The printing presses are waiting, we are told firmly by our three minders, and we need to plan an official launch. Radio 4 wants an interview for its Today programme and The Sunday Times is interested.

We come up with the obvious:

"Minority Arts in Britain?"

"Boring!"

"How about 'Black Arts in Britain'?"

"They'll think we're witches."

"The Silenced Minority?"

"But we're not silent. Anything but."

"The Ethnic Arts of Britain?"

'Too clunky. We want something with a bit of character. That says something about what we're arguing...

"And don't forget it is about *arts*!"

But the more we talk the worse it gets: we're getting caught up in a quagmire of laboured and increasingly bad ideas. It's getting late and I can see Shantu's anxious about her train home to Leicester. There's a frustrated sigh. Will we ever have a name for it? In the meantime, one of our official minders – a crisp-minded quiet pedant – has been thoughtfully scribbling. He raises his head and asks,

"How about – "The Arts that Britain Ignores?"" He lays down his pen and waits.

We mull it over, roll it around and see how it feels in the mouth. It feels… yes, it feels… OK. We look at each other cautiously. But Norman doesn't wait. "I like it," he says decisively. "It sounds good. Strong. Just knock out the word 'that."

We nod: 'The Arts Britain Ignores' – it has a ring. We have a name. It's all done.

But there's more to come.

"How are you going to make sure it's effective?" asks the quiet minder. "You don't want it to just sit on a shelf?"

The evidence we've gathered is strong. Surely it must talk for itself? But I look around the table and see we aren't at all certain. It could gather dust, after all our work.

"An organisation," Taiwo speaks up. "A group who'll chase the report, who'll call organisations to account. That's what we need."

I think of the hundreds of people who've been involved with the report, and all the people I've been encouraging to see they have a right to be heard. "We've come so far. We have to stay with it," Shantu says.

There 's no disagreement. After all these months, we have become like family. I have become family, committed to the Britain we now know intimately. We have uncovered it together and in the process we have found we have a new role too. We thought at the back of our minds that we were visitors but actually we are citizens.

An organisation, to push the recommendations further, to make sure that we all stay visible. Keep going.

When I get into our office I can see straightaway that something's wrong. Veronica looks round only briefly as I come into the room. She is filing, banging the drawers shut, in and out with a huge clang. There's nothing like a filing cabinet for demonstrating mood. I daren't ask what's up, her face is so closed and tight with that formal haughty look that I've come to recognise in the past few months our organisation's been running.

I put my bag down beside my desk. Veronica is meanwhile still creating a small storm with the filing cabinet. I look at my desk, She has stacked the mail there in an over-neat stack in a way that somehow manages to look accusing.

"Sorry I'm a bit late."

"Hm..." She sits down and starts going through the day book. I hold my breath.

Then, without looking up, she says almost casually. 'There's a letter for you. From the Huttons."

"Really?" I'm surprised. Usually Mary Hutton waves out of her window when she sees us coming through the garden gate on the way to the little annex we're renting. What's the point of writing us a letter?

"They're giving us notice."

"What!"

"She put it through the door and I opened it."

"But they said we could stay for as long as we liked."

It reads really strangely – formally typed, addressed to 'Minorities Arts Advisory Service (MAAS): attn N Khan, Director'. "'With regret', it says, and 'due to unforeseen' and 'termination'.

"Something must have turned up," I say dubiously, reading it through again. "It's very odd..."

There is a snort from Veronica. Then – "'Something turned up,'" she says sarcastically. "They don't like black people. That's what it's all about."

"No, surely..." She ignores me.

"I always had that funny feeling with her, you know. She'd never look me in the eye. Never. Never once. Always so polite and so English." She is boiling with rage.

"And this area – no black people here at all. I don't think she liked people seeing me come to her house."

Under the rage she is deeply upset. When we first met, I thought Veronica was so ebullient and capable and unsinkable. I loved her bravado and her wonderful laugh. But underneath I can hear there is such fragility.

I am shaken too. We've got such a snug little custom-made office here, everything set up. We've stepped into it as if it had been made to measure. We're just getting MAAS established. "'Maas' as in carnival," we'd all said when we decided to set it up at the end of 'The Arts Britain Ignores'. And 'mas' too because in Spanish it means 'bigger'. "And we are bigger!"

"We are massive!"

Massive or not, we are homeless.

I read it again. "They're giving us a month's notice!"

"Not a minute more in this place. No way!" she declares hotly. "We're out at the end of the week. I'm not staying here a minute longer. I'm not putting up with racism."

"I suppose we can always go back to Grafton Road, to the spare room there, where we started off."

But there's an au pair living there now. "Listen. I'll sort something out. I've got a meeting this morning down near Oxford Street. Let's talk when I get back."

The bus down to the Angel is crowded and I have to stand. Veronica's adamant and she's right, but we don't have many options. We could go back to the community centre where we had a free desk for a time, but their place is due to be demolished and a fancy new arts centre come up in its place. And it was cold and draughty. Let's face it, our little office – all mod cons on tap – has spoiled us. Damn, damn, damn.

Mortimer Street turns out to be north of Oxford Street. It's a busy rarefied area full of shops and outlets catering to the fashion trade – samples, outfits, belts, accessories. Vans are regularly drawing up outside and lads emerging with big cartons. Young women pass by purposefully, their arms draped with scores of dresses in plastic bags. They are all impossibly slim, with long straight upper-class hair – I heard somewhere that they ironed it: can that be true? – and heavily made-up Bambi eyes. There is a bustle and urgency and sense of self-importance about the place that is quite unlike MAAS and our Islington backwater. Bracing, it is.

The little doorway between two shops is very modest, so modest I pass it twice before I find it. And the stairs up to the first floor office of Star Travels are definitely grubby. 'Curtains and kippers' Mother would say. I'm not at all sure I'd want to travel with this agency. Just as well that's not why I'm here.

But it turns out that it is a wild goose chase anyhow. Mr Gill had heard of MAAS and had thought we could fund his Punjabi literary society. We work out quickly we've been at cross purposes and we actually don't have anything to say to each other.

But as I leave the back office where Mr Gill is sitting, I catch a glimpse of something unusual and very interesting in the larger front office. "Might I look?"

Gill edges his way out from behind his desk that is overflowing with bills and invoices and lading documents and very old-looking tour brochures. He is a large middle-aged man with a paunch and has to negotiate the desk and stacks of cardboard boxes very carefully. I look at the boxes. "We are also a trading company," he explains.

His front office is larger and looks straight out onto the street. It has a couple of empty desks in it and a filing cabinet. But the thing I had glimpsed was the right-hand wall. It is covered, top to bottom, with a mural – not a painted one, but made up of shapes cut out of jewel-coloured hessian. They form a stylised picture of gods and animals and is the most beautiful thing I have seen in ages and certainly the most unexpected.

"A young boy, an artist," says Gill, "Ishwar. He asked permission."

"Is this his office then?"

"No, no, he just comes here sometimes. It is unused. Hardly used."

I don't believe I have heard – what I think I have heard.

"I am not here very much. My business takes me abroad a great deal. It is a waste of course."

Yes, I have heard correctly.

Would he, might he, consider renting the front room to us?

Yes, he would. And if he's out, he says, we could use his back office for meetings if we need.

As easy as that. It beggars all belief. I chortle all the way back to Oxford Street. It is magic. I am dreaming: I must be. But no, I am here and awake. I can see my reflection in the window of the sandwich bar. I look stunned.

What a change – from sedate and quiet Islington where hardly a person is to be seen in the daytime, to this rackety sharp entrepreneurial place, and to an office that is decorated in a style fit for a king. Kubla Khan and your pleasure dome, step down.

We have our first committee meeting in our new office – Peter perched on Veronica's desk, Taiwo and Ravi on chairs we've borrowed from Mr Gill. We all feel better off in Oxford Street, less marooned in gentility. And it suits us better. After all, the work that we're doing is all about movement and change, with the sharpness and immediacy that all migrants have to acquire. Now we are in an area that coasts on entrepreneurialism, rooted in the Jewish rag trade and up-market schmutter. It fits because we are re-inventing ourselves and we need to be in a place that is poised like this, on its toes.

Veronica is happier too. Mr Gill is eating out of her hand. He is a shy and secretive man who comes and goes at irregular intervals but she has tamed him with her buoyancy and competence. When Christmas comes he ceremonially presents us both with hairbrushes. We compare notes afterwards and believe that they are samples.

We are in the centre of things here, and people come to visit us. Arts administrators, artists, poets all come trooping up our narrow stairs. Old friends find us – black writers from CAM, Tara Rajkumar who is planning to set up her own Indian dance academy – a first. A trio of good-looking young Indians turn up to talk about the theatre group they have formed in response to Blair Peach's murder in Southall. A young Taiwanese man charms us with his plans for a tai-chi based version of the Chinese folk fable, 'The Monkey King'. Can we help him, he asks, to find funding?

Our own funding is tenuous. "Do you remember the first grant?" Veronica asks, "When the man from Marks and Spencer turned up, when we were in the spare room in Grafton Road?"

"You told him straight to his face that you knew he'd think we didn't look professional and I nearly died!"

"But that's what he liked..."

"He said, 'That's exactly why I'm going to recommend you get funding'. He said he 'could see our passion'."

We high-five each other.

Each time now when we send off another funding application, we both touch the envelope ceremonially, to give it luck.

"I feel as if we are sitting on a traffic island," I say to Veronica as we take a break between phone calls.

"Meaning?"

"We seem to spend our time directing people – sending festivals to music groups, theatres to black actors. Arts boards that want committee members."

In the spring, Oliver Bennett who's an arts officer with the regional arts board based in Manchester gets in touch. His board wants to respond to 'The Arts Britain Ignores'. They know we're against setting up separate Ethnic Arts Sub-Committees. He is proposing to call a meeting of groups and artists in the region to see what better ways there might be: can I come and talk at it?

Oliver has taken the basement of a community centre for the meeting. I can hear the noise of conversation at the top of the stairs and, when I get down to the bottom, it's clear that there's not a spare seat in the house. Here and there in the throng, I catch sight of people that look familiar. Many of them are people I spoke to when I was travelling the country for "The Arts Britain Ignores'. I can see Dr Desai and a few of his committee from the Indian Association, Ivan Rawluk from the magnificent Ukrainian Centre, a group from the Moss Side Youth Centre. Oliver's spread his net wider – the carnivalisters from Leeds are there, and a group of turbaned Sikhs, new to me. And so many more. The room is full to bursting with people, cultures, artforms, ages. People are pushing the chairs closer to be able to get more in. There's an air of expectation as Oliver in his jeans and sweatshirt ambles to the front to welcome everyone. He's got a programme but it's rapidly junked because too many people want to get up and talk. It's as if they've been reined in so long they can't wait any longer.

It all tumbles out. Frustration, aspiration, need. Need for space, for recognition, outlets, funding. "Yes," people shout – Caribbean, Polish, Cypriot, Indian, African, all their testimonies reinforce the other. There is such a consensus, and as this grows so the energy in the room rises and the sense of a new strength and confidence. Oliver has totally lost control of the agenda but no-one worries about that, certainly not Oliver. "How about regional branches of MAAS?" he suggests. Why not? Suddenly the world seems bigger. We all understand each other, outsiders seeing that we could actually be insiders.. Language and history, no barrier. We have the same aspirations. Above all – and this is what really is the insight – we are not alone.

I can feel electricity running along my veins – really feel it, crackling and fizzing. I can hear and feel the emotion in the room. It is a sense of common discovery and a rush of air comes with it that has an unmistakeable sense of release. I turn to Oliver to see if he gets this too, but I can't find any words. I am too proud that I have had a hand in this extraordinary occurrence. Invisible no longer, I think: silent no longer. Arts and artists that Britain can ignore? No longer. But also, we can input. We can remake Britain.

When I get home late at night, John is up watching television, a kebab from our local takeaway on a plate on the floor beside him. With one hand, he's absently shaking hot pepper sauce over it, without looking.

"That Makarios," he says admiringly as I come into the room, "Just come and watch this. He's up to his tricks again, bastard! What did I tell you...?"

"Is all well? Amelia asleep?"

"What? Oh, yes."

"Ingrid around?"

"Who? Oh, I dunno. Gone out, I think. Look at that. Fucking Denktash – doesn't have a chance. And he knows it!"

The Cyprus problem, continuing.

"I'll go and check on Amelia. Then I'll turn in. I'm really tired."

"OK. Good night."

CHAPTER FIFTEEN
1979

It's a struggle going into work in the winter when John and little Amelia are snug at home in the warm, He's playing her The Grateful Dead. "She likes it," he says proudly. "She's got taste. She gets it from me." Christmas is over and shop windows are full of reduced clothes looking limp and sad on hangers. It's damp and cold and I can see my breath as I'm jostled by avid bargain-hunters who are also cross. A sharp intake of breath as I bump into one of them, but when I turn round she has already gone. Even the street vendors are huddled up and miserable, the air round their wagons heavy with that over-sweet cloying smell of vanilla and waffles. There are no takers.

Oxford Street, Upper Regent Street and then into Mortimer Street and I can breathe again. Here's our little secret door tucked away between a sandwich bar and a wholesale fashion outlet that's closed till February. It's a relief to get here and as I climb the dingy stairs to our office, the sounds of Oxford Street grow faint.

"The bulbs have gone again," I start to say, but Veronica's on the phone. Day after day the stairs annoy me. One day someone will fall down and then they'll take notice. No point talking to Mr Gill. He's hardly ever here. A rum travel agents. I can see why he let the front office to us with such alacrity. And all the time I thought I'd engineered a coup.

Veronica signs heavily and puts the phone down.

"What's up?"

She clicks her tongue in that very expressive Jamaican way. "That man – tcha! You'd think he'd have some idea, all this time in this country."

"Lewis?" I need hardly say it. She tosses her head in an aggravated way.

"No point even talking about it. I'll just get too vexed. Let me make us both a cup of tea." She goes over to the little cupboard between the two offices and I dump my bag and papers on the desk opposite.

"Biscuit?"

"Better not."

"Go on, you've got nothing to worry about. Look at me... They're those yummy ones I picked up in Marks. One can't hurt."

"Oh... OK. That was hard. Slimming starts tomorrow."

She's in her perfect-PA mode today. I can tell just by the way she is dressed, neat and slightly over-formal. Sometimes it's jeans and sweatshirt, but not today. I sit down as she brings me my cup of tea. All this feels a bit odd. We wanted nothing to do with bosses and hierarchy in the *Hustler*. Hierarchy, we all agreed, was the enemy and oppressive structures create class. Everybody should take a part in decision-making, we believed. And I still do. But now here I am, I suppose I'm a boss and I don't like it very much. Fortunately Veronica likes filing cabinets and day-books and bustles round our mini office. She has somehow managed to get a memorable phone number out of the phone company. I never knew you could do that. "You've got to sweet-talk them, man." She sets us up with special caddies for tea and for coffee and for sugar and she clips about efficiently as the kettle starts to whistle. But another time it's a jeans day and we eat biscuits and gossip and compare notes about potty-training and our toddlers' first words.

"Don't forget you've got a meeting with the Arts Council at 11am." She hands me a new red folder with 'MAAS" printed on the cover. There is just one sheet of paper inside telling me how to get to Piccadily.

"And that man from South Yorkshire called again, what's his name?"

"Rowntree?"

"That's the one. He still wants to fix a date for you to go and talk to their Culture Committee."

'I'll call him later." I look at the book where we log phone calls. "Feroze Mahmud called?"

"Oh yes, I meant to mention that. I know you won't be pleased. He wants to come off the Arts Council's Music Panel."

"But he's been only on it for a few months!" And it was a coup getting him there in the first place.

Feroze answers the phone immediately. I think he must have been waiting next to it.

"I'm really really sorry." He's a sweet-mannered, gentle man, so deeply steeped in Indian classical music it's awe-inspiring. But today even his voice sounds small.

"But why? It's really important to have a voice on that panel. Otherwise it's all western music."

"Yes, Naseemji, I do know."

"So, then?"

165

There's a little sigh from the other end of the line. "I didn't like to tell you this before, but.." He stops, and I can hear a sound of him swallowing, and then he continues, in a rush.

"This is what happens. Every time the Arts Council officers bring up an application that's from a non-western group or musician, all the other panel members put down their papers and they just turn and look at me. They expect me to be an expert on every kind of music that they call 'ethnic'. I know Indian classical music. It's my home. My heart is there. But all the other forms I know nothing about. So many! But they seem to think that I am the one to tell them who they should give money to or not. It makes me feel very very uneasy...

"I know it is a responsibility, and I was honoured you put my name forward, but please do understand why..."

What can I do but accept?

Veronica isn't surprised,

"I saw it coming," she says loftily. "He's got no backbone, that man."

But what does it all mean? Feroze isn't the only one who feels lost in Arts Council land. It's as if he's got the wrong phrasebook. Norman and Taiwo can speak the language but even they're struggling to establish their black theatre companies. "Go and play to the community," the Arts Council says to them. When Mustafa Matura's new play was at the ICA and a review suggested it should have been staged in Brixton, the playwright exploded.

"Patronising," agrees Veronica. "Are we add-ons to the Brits and their culture? Don't we have a place in the mainstage?"

It's only been a year since 'The Arts Britain Ignores' was published and now where are we? None of us have forgotten our debates that went on around the CRC's polished board-room table.

"Are you sure you don't want to recommend a special Ethnic Minority Arts Committee for the Arts Council with its own budget?" one of our minders had prompted. There's no question about it. We were all adamant, even with the lure of money. And that's saying something.

"No marginalisation!"

"No ghettoisation!"

"And while we're about it, let's ditch the 'Minority Arts' thing too. We're not minor."

Whoever thought we were minor?" Day by day the entries in our daily office log grow in number. A few weeks in, we already need a new book. Some people say they are "minority arts", some don't. More and more groups and people are coming out of hiding. We provide schools with workshop leaders, festivals with musicians, curators with artists. Peter's music group is touring and wherever he goes he urges people to contact us. Radio London signs me up to do a weekly Asian show and Veronica joins Alex Pascall on Radio Black Londoners. The phone rings and rings. But then Veronica's childminder gives up and Ingrid goes back to Germany and I am between au pairs. We struggle with crises at home and squeezing in answering ever more queries. Men, we suspect, would not experience these pressures.

The phone is ringing as I stumble up the stairs, late. It's hard to see – the bulbs have still not been replaced.

"It's been going non-stop for the past half hour," says Mr Gill who's here on one of his rare mysterious visits. He doesn't look pleased. The door to his back office closes with a disapproving click.

"We can't continue like this."

"It's like that sketch where people run around trying to stop plates falling off poles."

Oliver rings from Manchester. "Have you thought any more of regional branches?" Not a very welcome thought right now. But, yes, OK, Oliver, it makes sense – one in Birmingham for starters.

"And in Liverpool," insists Norman when we bring it up in MAAS' trustees' meeting.

"We are going to call it SWEAT," say people in Cardiff when they ring to say they want to start a branch.

"Really? Are you sure?"

"It stands for South Wales Ethnic Arts Team."

"It's OK for Birmingham, but what about us, here in the East Midlands?" ask people from Nottingham querulously. A middle-aged turbaned Sikh calls from Glasgow. He has an Asian dance group ("Very popular") where all the girls are Scottish and wear tartan saris. He wants to start MAAS Scotland.

"It's not spinning plates," says Veronica, "It's hanging on to a bloody runaway horse."

When it works – when we can cling on – it's wonderful, even though the effort of pushing the new work into old structures nearly defeats us. Do the British really want it, we sometimes wonder. But something is surely growing and we have helped to push it on its way. Black Book Fairs, grassroots publishing, new plays, film and video – and new locations. On Wednesday I find my way into the middle of a run-down housing estate behind Kings Cross station. A black architect has turned a disused church into a full-blown cultural centre complete with theatre, exhibition space, library. There's a sound of banging and a smell of new wood.

"I'm looking for Oscar..." He emerges from a back office, a small man his hair speckled with sawdust.

The very next day, a courteous South Indian gentleman, his forehead striped with puja marks, climbs our risky office stairs. He informs us he's just bought a huge church in West Kensington for a major Indian cultural centre.

"I took a suitcase full of pound notes to the estate agents," he relates tranquilly, as if it was an everyday affair. Veronica and I look at each other open-mouthed.

There is a change in the air. All my committee – the old 'Arts Britain Ignores' team – notice it. Not so long ago, communities were hanging passionately onto their roots and retaining culture. But now the focus is turning more and more to the strains and experience of living here. 'Everyone has a story to tell," say community artists, and people are eager to tell their stories. They have kept them hidden for so long.

And what stories. I've never been to Tooting before, but here I am, in a grotty local authority centre full of notices about inoculations and library times, for a play by a new Asian theatre group. It's been written by its performers, and the synopsis sounds deeply melodramatic. My ex-critic's antennae twitch. A young girl does what a lot of Asian teens are doing right now –going to school with her home gear stuffed in her satchel, and then making her way to a day-time Asian dance scene where she changes in the toilet. But a lad is also there from her street and has always fancied her. "Sleep with me," he says, "Or else I'll tell on you to your parents." She gets pregnant. She can't face the repercussions and kills herself.

Melodramatic? No, all true, say the trio of recent graduates fervently – Jatinder, Owais and Sunil – who've just started Tara Arts. It really happened. It shook them all and it made them think. How could disclosure be worse than death? What does it say about their own families and Asian values as a whole? And so I sit on the edge of my seat in that obscure hall, hearing and seeing things I have never thought to see or hear in an English theatre. The downside of Asianness. Not just the energy, warmth and rootedness that I know but the tyranny of convention, the fear of difference, the gossip, hypocrisies, snobbery and the ubiquitous army of prying aunties. Watching it feels slightly risky: like reading a forbidden book. I look around to see if other people are experiencing the same sort of frisson. In my own mind I can hear Abba and the Indian Association, disapproving:

"You don't wash your dirty laundry in public."

Tara doesn't care about all that and, yes, it is exhilarating. It's fresh air and I sit up straight. And how different the Tara trio are too. I am used to conservative older Indians who cling together in clans. Secretive and mildly apologetic. But these ones have confidence – even a touch of arrogance. They come to visit us at MAAS and they perch on the edge of our desks, talking over each other like young lords and dropping cigarette ash in Veronica's pretty saucers. They might each be headed, they say, for the law or public administration, or maybe the theatre, if they so choose. They're super bright, and not only that, every single one of them is incredibly good-looking in a clean-cut dashing sort of way. I have to restrain myself from licking their chukka boots. Gosh. I fall in love with all of them straightaway.

And maybe the Taras are the future? After all, it's 1976 not 1955, and a new generation is just graduating. Even the Tory Party's just elected a woman leader. When I think of our old Indian Association, a sort of sepia haze settles around them now. I can see them on a quayside, huddled up in their good quality winter coats, getting fainter and fainter in the distance as our boat sails on, until the mist makes even their outlines indistinguishable. Old-timers. The ship's horn blares with the thrill of movement. A new breed of home-grown Asians is arriving on the scene: bold, critical, confident; able to make their own mix, looking around them and not backwards. And good-looking. I hum to myself as the three young Taras clatter heedlessly down the stairs.

"I think..." and then the phone rings.

It's my mother. "At last! I've been trying for days to find you. I think you forget we exist."

"Sorry, Mother, I'm in the middle of—"

"You are always busy."

It's well into the evening before I can phone Mother back. John's been drafted onto the Friends of Cyprus committee and is at a meeting to discuss their strategy after the Turkish invasion. The new au pair, Jane, is out with her boyfriend. Amelia is safely in her cot, sleeping in her customary way – on her front, knees tucked up under her like a yoga pose, right thumb in her mouth and the left one over her ear. It's as if she wants to create a perfect circuit.

How quiet it is. The sound of a small child breathing. From the floor below, Mozart's Clarinet Quintet on the record player, the slow movement.

No-one phoning. No-one arriving frustrated at not getting funding. Rain outside, but not heavy. I tiptoe downstairs, leaving the door slightly ajar.

Mother's less cross by now.

"Where's Abba?"

"Out. Doing a few visits after surgery," she says. I have a sense of her by the telephone in the hall, batting her cigarette smoke away as we talk.

"I want to talk to you. It's all too much for him. He really should let the younger doctors do it. But all the patients want him. And all this business with the Betta – you know it went bankrupt? – it's on his mind. I can tell. And then there's the new Jaguar. We really can't afford it, and it's not necessary."

Ah, this is familiar territory. Every year, every motor show, every new model: the same temptation. It is the apple on the tree and both Abba and Anwar are drawn to it.

Each year, poring over manuals, visiting showrooms, revisiting showrooms. It's like the early stages of a mating dance. "We're just looking. There's no harm in that..." Endlessly and exhaustively, they debate the merits of each mark: the variations, the improvements, the speed, the fuel consumption.

"It's not in the class of the XK120. Or the E type."

"But it does have a 12 cylinder engine."

"Hmm, that's true. And three-speed automatic transmission."

He flirts every year with the prospect. No he won't, yes he might. It is exasperating.

"But Abba, you don't need it."

"Yes, I know... But Anwar will be really disappointed if I don't buy it."

"He should be slowing down," Mother resumes. 'Especially now he's got a pacemaker.' And then she stops, "I'd better go, I can hear his car. I'll speak to you later. But when are you coming to see us?"

"In a few weeks, Easter. We're going to Osea just before it."

But she's gone.

Then, the next morning, Abba also phones. I can tell he's in the surgery because the air has a formal static sound quality. I can almost smell formaldehyde.

"Good, I've got you," he says briskly and launches in his brisk doctor's voice straight into business. No small talk. "I want..." But then he breaks off and talks to someone in the room with him:

"No. Tell her to wait.

"No, I can't see her now... I don't care. That's not my business... She's got to wait. Like everyone else."

He sounds tense. I am glad I'm not that needy patient.

"It's about your mother..." he comes back to me.

"I spoke to her last night." He does not hear this.

"This smoking, non-stop. It's undermining her health. She'll be back in hospital in no time at this rate. I had to put her on oxygen last time."

There is the sound of his surgery door opening. "I've got to go. Give her a ring – just talk to her. See what you can do."

Fat chance of success I think. And I think he knows that too. But what can I do? Just watch them, both of them, getting older and frailer.

Arriving at Osea, with its reeking prehistoric causeway, the world drops away. Ageing parents, confusing work where obstacles seem to increase daily, my own non-stop fatigue. I stand at the head of the rise that overlooks the estuary as we wait for the cold grey tide to roll back. I breathe in fresh and neutral air. If only I could bring Mother here. Here it's a blank canvas, clean and washed clear. The sky is big, a few gulls high up. We'd slip the anchors of our past here – her addiction (let's be honest, that's what it is), my in-between half-identity, the tangles of marriage. The high clear nothingness sweeps things away.

When night falls on Osea we hunker down in our one-storey clapboard house; an old apple tree taps at the window as the sea breezes rise. Amelia is down in her carrycot and I start to cook spaghetti while John fiddles with the radio. Finally after a number of buzzes and high frequency squeaks he finds the 9 o'clock news. He sits up sharply.

"Fucking hell," he exclaims, "Wilson's resigned!" He gets up and walks up and down around the little front room. "Fuck!" He opens the front door as if he looks for the crowds out there that will be aghast. He's all ready to spring into journo action, to dictate his Wilson memories to copytakers, to contact the news desk. But there's nothing he can do. There's just one pay phone, in a locked office. And we can't get off the island anyhow because the tide won't go down for another eight hours.

We are cut off. What a relief.

Weddings should be happy.

There's something odd about this one. We drive up, the three of us, in good time and park in the narrow lane. I've never been to this church before and it's not the picturesque country church I'd expected. It's outside a village, true, but it's strangely squat and urban, in red brick.

But Abba is already there, at its door, looking resplendent in morning dress. He's tense and excited, won't settle, moves from one side of the open door to the other almost as if he was the groom. "Hello, sir!" he says jocularly to John and puts both hands out.

Behind us another car is drawing up and people come spilling out. The Sharmas, I think, or maybe the Dasguptas. Abba flaps his hands at us in a mildly distracted way. 'Your mother's inside. I told her to go and sit down. Hurry up – go and join her.'

I wish he would calm down.

"Who are all these people?" I whisper as we slide into the pew beside Mother.

"God knows," she mutters. She's looking pale. "Your father. He just wouldn't stop. He's invited just about everyone we've ever met."

She stops to draw breath and I shift Amelia's weight to a space between John and me.

"Half the old Indian Association and the staff from all three surgeries and even the medical reps who come round with samples – they're here too. I don't know half the people he's invited."

The church is filling up with people who are looking around as if they are in some strange foreign country. A lot of them are Indian. "But where's the bride's family?" I whisper. There seems only a handful. But Mother's still craning restlessly around to look behind her.

"It's getting on. He ought to come and sit down. He never does anything right!"

More people clatter into the echoey church. I can see my cousin Chand, with her husband and her two children, all the way from London. They wave in a jolly fashion.

"John," Mother pleads, "You go and make him come."

John returns shrugging defeat. Abba is far too wired. Inside the church the organ starts to play in a snuffly cautious sort of way and people shift wondering if they ought to stand. But so far there's no bride. Surely Abba will come and sit down now? At the front Anwar and his best man are standing stiffly with their backs to us. It feels like a game. We might creep up and suddenly shout "Boo!" John pokes Amelia and makes faces at her. "Shh!" I hiss. I need her to last for the whole service. I don't want to have to take her out.

Finally Abba's here, just as the organ ramps up into a triumphal entry march and Katherine and her father start to process down the aisle.

It feels happier and more like a wedding when we get to the reception in a big hotel in a nearby village. The entrance has a canopy over it festooned with bobbing silver balloons. Anwar and Katherine emerge from their limousine shedding confetti at every step and make their way through the throngs of well-wishers. I find a place to park the carrycot for when Amelia goes to sleep. But right now she loves the balloons and the crowds and people patting her. She's a sociable child who smiles at everyone and is happy for quite some time to be passed around from arm to arm. At times I even wonder where she's gone. Waitresses appear with trays of champagne.

Mother tugs at my arm. "Come along. I've got to powder my nose," she declares. "Come with me." Amelia is back with John now. "I just need a quick cigarette."

We find a pair of French windows that lead out onto a side bit of the hotel grounds and duck out. Mother sits down on a low wall with a sigh. She takes off her wedding hat and pulls her packet of Players out of her handbag.

"That's better." We can just hear the distant sound of conversation and laughter. To one side there must be the kitchen because there's noise of cutlery and glass. It's slightly breezy and fresh.

"I'll be glad when it's all over."

"What a good thing John and I didn't do this whole thing."

"Not at all," she snaps. "I'm never going to forgive you for that. Going off with none of us there to a registry office. Our only daughter. Everyone in Birmingham commented."

I should have held my tongue. It took her six weeks to talk to me again.

There's a sound of movement from inside,

"We'd better be going back. They must be going through for the meal."

There's much jostling and friendly pushing as we all settle down around the long table, the length of the conservatory. If people didn't know each other before they do now and the decibel level rises in a cheerful happy way. In the middle of the long table sit Anwar, looking sheepish but pleased, and his wife. My little brother! Katherine twitches back her veil. She's an angular young woman taller than my brother, and she doesn't look wholly comfortable in bridal white.

Amelia has fallen asleep on John's shoulder and he passes her over to me. I tiptoe out and lay her in her carrycot in a side-room. "We'll keep an eye on her," whisper the waitresses who are passing to and fro all the time.

"Wasn't there another woman he wanted to marry? What did Anwar do with her?" asks John far too loudly as I go back to sit beside him.

"Hush! Someone might hear."

"I think we should be told, don't you? I'm going to have to ask him. Maybe this is a Muslim thing." And he moves as if to stand up.

"Don't you dare!"

He's being naughty and is delighted I rise to it.

We're past the melon stage and are tucking into the coronation chicken. And then, as the plates are cleared for Pavlova, Brian, Anwar's best man, gets up and tells a number of droll tales about his old school pal. Katherine's father says a few standard words of gratitude for having his daughter taken off his hands. Then unexpectedly Abba gets up. I have a sense of foreboding and I can see that Mother does too.

He is not a great speaker. He rambles and on this occasion is full of emotion. How proud he is of his son, he starts off: what a lot of struggle Anwar's gone through, how determined to be a lawyer, not Abba's choice – he had always wanted him to be a doctor to follow in his footsteps after all he has spent so many years building up his practice for a child to take it on but what can you do children have their own wishes nowadays, they do what they want to do what can we as just parents do, our job is over, we are at the end..

His voice goes wavery and he chokes with emotion.

People lean forward and there is a sudden hush. Mother puts her hand on his arm but he shakes it off. He struggles on.

"All my life I have worked hard, so hard... building up..."

No-one says anything. The room is silent, tense. Half of the people there know about his heart attack. Is it going to happen again, here?

Then Dr Mohan – kindly moon-faced man – gets up and in his ponderous way moves towards Abba. He starts to applaud as he walks towards Abba and everyone joins in. He puts his arm around Abba's shoulders.

"We all know this, Wasi" he says, and gently eases him down. People clap. Finally Abba, Inshah Allah, sits and dabs his eyes with his crisp white hotel napkin.

"I need air," Mother says sotto voce. Chand and I discreetly pull our chairs back and follow her to the anteroom where Amelia is still fast asleep. None of us say anything but my own heart is racing.

"I'll get you some water, Mrs Khan," says Chand. Mother and I sink into the deep sofas.

"This was my first Christian wedding," Chand says conversationally when she returns.

"They're not all like this." Thank heaven.

"Such an important day for Wasi Chacha – his son's marriage" she goes on in her comfortable way. "Siddiqui and I were really honoured to be called and the children were so excited. Lubna wanted to know if she could be a bridesmaid. You saw I made long dresses for both us, matching dresses?"

"Were you there for Nafees and Maqbool's marriage?'

I remember their marriage in Hyderabad – the marvellous high-octane glitz of it. The wedding cooks that arrived on tongas and parked in the courtyard for days with their vast copper pots. The friends and relatives that steadily arrived from every part of Pakistan and beyond. The honour that the massive three-day wedding brought to the family. Poor Abba, I suddenly realise, having to settle for this pallid cut-rate substitute. And such an important day.

'No,' Chand sighed. "I would have loved to have been there. But we couldn't afford the airfare. Siddiqui's job didn't pay much then, and we needed every penny. Of course – he's such a good man – he did say, '*You must go*,' but how could I? And I'd started to work too."

Mother stirs. Her colour looks better. "I'll go back in.

"I'll wait a bit. Amelia's due to wake soon. She'll need a feed."

It's cosy here in the little sitting room, just Chand and me, with only the muted noises of the company in the dining room and occasional snuffles from my sleeping child.

"What work were you doing?"

"Oh, it's a long story, Apa."

We settle down.

"When I came to England, I knew nothing. You know I never had any education. They didn't think it was important for girls back in Pakistan."

"I'm glad you're here, but why didn't you get married in Pakistan?"

"My father had taken a second wife – a really nasty piece of work and my mother had a feeling she'd marry me off to somebody unkind, somebody who'd beat me. Just for spite."

"Could she?"

"Oh yes. And then Ammi heard about Siddiqui on the family grapevine. He was 35 and wanted a Pakistani wife, and she thought he'd be steady and I'd be safe. So she fixed the marriage and sent me to England. "

"But you were so young – fourteen?"

"Old enough for marriage. And Siddiqui, I must tell you, he was very kind. He showed me how to do things, how to cook and run the house – well, it was just a room at first. He's a good man."

I can believe it. He's a sweet man, not a man you'd spot in a crowd – plain, bespectacled, ordinary, and probably looking middle-aged from late youth. But with a modest kindly demeanour.

"I managed to get a job in a laundrette folding the clothes and sheets when they come out of the machines. They were burning hot! So hot, Apa, I used to get blisters all over my hands." She holds her plump brown hands up – well healed now – and her rows of bangles clink.

Amelia stirs and we both lower our voices. Chand strokes her back and she turns over and relaxes. 'Beautiful child. Mashallah,' she says. Faint sounds of applause drift in from the dining room. They must be cutting the cake.

"But blistered hands..!"

"Yes, that was bad," she agrees and with such an absence of bitterness that I am awestruck. "But then," and her voice picks up. "The laundrette owner – a Jewish man – realised I was naturally good at maths and asked me to keep the accounts. In the end I was doing all his books."

"Are you still there?"

"Oh no, didn't you know? I've started my own driving school. "

"That's amazing, Chand!"

"You have to just get on with it, don't you? If you're prepared to work hard in this country, you can succeed. Mahshallah, things have turned out well. And well, what's the alternative?"

There's an argument going on between Veronica and our new suave London Co-Ordinator, Patrick, when I go back into the MAAS office.

"But you can see their side," Patrick's insisting in his usual reasonable tone. I strongly suspect he could be stirring her up.

"It's crap," Veronica says firmly. "Total crap! Listen to this," she turns to me. "I know you'll be on my side. We just got a call from a drama group – it's some African name or other, I forget what. Anyway, they're Caribbean. They're not African at all."

"What!" Patrick protests.

She waves him aside, "This is it – this group, they got a grant from the London Arts Council and now the Council wants to know how it was spent. And just tell me, what's wrong with that? But the group won't give them their books. They're claiming African culture doesn't operate in that way. They're more 'holistic' or whatever... They are 'closer to the sources of life – per-lease!" She rolls her eyes. "Well, call me old-fashioned but I think it's just an excuse for poor management."

I think so too but Patrick doesn't think so and when I talk to Peter Blackman later he disagrees too. "They were right. I'm with them all the way. Absolutely! Their mistake was applying to the Arts Council in the first place. That was the mistake. They should have gone to the community. They surrendered control. It was racism, even if the Arts Council didn't see it."

History and colonialism and slavery – all that undeclared undergrowth is only an inch and a thought away. The Arts Council sets up training schemes because it's true a lot of the work does suffer from not having had exposure or that simple process of trying, failing, learning and improving. But:

"We're always being trained," say people bitterly.

"Never getting opportunities."

"Why do we have to change? What about white people?"

And it's true. I look again at the stats – the ones that Norman quoted – and I have a sense of a mismatch and walls that are not even recognised.

A year goes by, and more. MAAS's branches grow and new younger people do surface to run them. But fundraising seems never to end and I am tired of complaints and complaining and of focussing on powerlessness rather than potential. At times I think of Chand's resilience, and Abba's stories of sitting on roundabouts in his home town in India along with other students to revise because their homes had no electricity.

In the summer I discover I am pregnant. I count up on my fingers – hmm.

"Perhaps we should call him or her 'Osea'."

"Poor sod," says John.

It's time to take a break.

And it lasts, and I explore different avenues with a public sector consultancy as Amelia and George (not 'Osea') grow up. We outgrow Kentish Town and put an offer on a house up the hill in leafier Hampstead. "A good property," Abba approves from his sickbed: his voice faint and laboured over the long-distance phone line. "I am very pleased..."

But early the very next morning when we are all still asleep, there's insistent banging and ringing at the front door. It's Chand and her husband Siddiqui who have driven up at first light from South London. Abba has died and no-one could reach me because our phone was off the hook.

And then one day, diversity calls out again. But do I really want to go back to the coal face?

PART FOUR
REINVENTING BRITAIN

CHAPTER SIXTEEN
1993

I could still be at home be chewing away on projects about changes to urban cultural policy, instead of here dragging my feet outside the gates of the prestigious Arts Council of England..

It sounded like a social call when Usha Prashar rang.

"How's John?" she asked, "And the family? George? Amelia? What's Amelia up to?"

"She's in New York. When she left Cambridge she got a fellowship with WPP to work there for a few years."

"Wonderful. Give her our best. Vijay still remembers her when she did work experience in his law firm when she was at school. We still talk about her at home."

I know that Usha – a very senior civil servant – is not a woman who makes social calls. There is an agenda here.

"Now," she resumes briskly. "I want to talk to you. You may have seen I've been appointed to sit on the Council of the Arts Council..."

"Well, not exactly..." I say cautiously.

"And frankly, Naseem, the whole issue of cultural diversity in the organisation has stalled. There's nothing going on."

She's right: The Arts Britain Ignores made an impact both on the Arts Council and the arts world at large, but almost twenty years on there is not enough to show. We are still two nations.

"And I intend to give a boost, Get it back on the road. And this is why I am calling you. I want you to help me."

I start to say something but Usha carries on. "I don't have much time to talk now, but I have persuaded them to create an officer post. And I want you to apply for it."

She can't see my expression but there is no way I could work for the Arts Council. It's not that I don't rate Usha's judgement – she is impressive and principled and wholly admirable. If I had to think of a living embodiment of public service, it would be Usha.

But even so... I am a hunter-gatherer and I like it. I enjoy uncertainty and not knowing what's around the corner.

"You know, Usha, I'm not sure I would be any good in the Arts Council," I start off cautiously. "I do seem to be better at independent things. You remember when I set up the alternative Festival of India to counter the official one? You supported me there."

"That's a different matter," she says briskly. "Think it over. You don't have to make up your mind now."

I say I will. But I already have.

"Have a look at the advertisement. It'll be in Monday's Guardian."

I look at it – 'Cultural Diversity Officer'. I do not apply.

Usha rings again. "We interviewed," she says, "But we couldn't appoint. We're going to re-advertise..."

"I really don't think so, Usha."

There's a pause, and I can hear her drawing a breath. Then she says with very measured emphasis,

"Listen to me. I want to tell you something." Pause. "If you want to change things, there is only one effective way – and that is *through institutions*. It is the only way. Listen to me, I know what I am talking about."

There's something gnomic or sibylline about her words. How can I not take her seriously, knowing how much she has achieved, and especially if I want to change things? And I do, I still do want to change things, even after all this time.

How can I escape all the memories, experiences and voices – the knowledge that I've gained more or less by osmosis, through operating between two worlds?

And if Usha doesn't know how change comes about, then who does? She speaks from lived knowledge and beneath her words is a deep and compelling moral seriousness.

But still...

"What do you think? Should I?" I ask a friend who's moved from managing dance companies to work within the Arts Council.

"Do it," she says. "Policy work is wonderful!"

'Wonderful'? That's not a word I'd ever have thought of...

But, "Go for it!" says Peter Blackman, old henchman of the 'Arts Britain Ignores' and MAAS days, when I go to talk it over with him in his flat.

"Really? But you worked there for a time and you left..."

"So I know what I am talking about. We need someone on the inside."

But now on the first day, outside its portals, I don't feel like a bold entryist. I've already chosen the wrong exit from Westminster underground, baffled by copious notices and hordes of tourists. What a fine start. I have to wait for ages while the lights change and the crowds hem me in as I try to thread my way over to Parliament and then down Great Peter Street. My stomach feels bad. I am actually nervous. There is no question about it. I feel like a newbie, and half look for my satchel. My clothes do not feel like my clothes. They are what I hope will pass for office wear.

It's a nice bright day but who cares? I hate the thought of being an employee. I am scared about losing my autonomy. I don't know how to operate in an organisation.

"Here's your pass," says the woman from Human Resources. "Sign here for it." Next she hands me an induction pack full of policies of the Arts Council of Great Britain, instructions for grievance procedures, guidance about fire drills and exit points. "Information on your pension will follow in due course."

My pension? I am not going to be here that long.

I have a desk. I have a computer. I have a pleasant competent PA called Louise, and I have a department boss. Everyone is as nice as pie. I am taken formally around the whole building, which in itself is confusing because every floor looks exactly like the other and pretty soon I am not sure if I am being introduced to literature officers or drama officers or visual arts officers. But everyone looks up from their computers wherever I am and smiles, and they all say welcome. I notice only two people who are not white.

The Arts Council is unlike anything else I have ever experienced. Time Out was all ramshackle talkative diversity, all of us on the same salary. Even an inglorious year at Good Housekeeping had a cosy feel to it because I was an editor in a little self-contained unit dealing with what was called 'Family Matters'. But the Arts Council is a big steely machine and I can't work out how it drives itself. It seems to move forward through meetings that operate at different levels like a series of cogs that turn and whirl steadily. They produce decisions that themselves slowly make their way down the system. The Art Council machine chomps and creates policies and churns out paper; it favours acronyms that I find opaque and mysterious. I ring to talk to the head of another department. "No, he's in SMOG," says his PA.

"'Senior Management Officers Group," Louise translates, smiling. "Not as grand as COG – that's Chief Officers' Group but pretty important. And then there's FOG too, that's Finance Officers' Group."

I digest this. "Why don't we start one called CDOG – pronounce it 'Sea Dog' – for Cultural Diversity Officers," I joke, because I like the cheek of it. However a group of just me doesn't sound too great.

It's hard to know what to make of it all. I ponder it day after day as I make my way back and forth between Great Peter Street and the Underground. Maybe all organisations are so bureaucratic. What do I know? I'm new to all this. Before I came I didn't even have any idea that my power would be directly related to where I am on the salary point scale. What innocence. But now I realise that the boost for diversity hasn't reached this far down: the Cultural Diversity Officer has been set low in the food chain; I'm at a sort of rice and dhal level.

From time to time, I manage to get to see Peter, who is my man outside, "It's like fighting with treacle."

'What's your budget?" he asks. I am embarrassed to admit that I didn't think to ask.

But Usha is right. Almost all mention of race and difference and culture has vanished off the agenda. This is a white place in terms of employees. And even more, I get to realise that for all the smiles, not everyone is glad that the post has been revived. The body language is clear, and so are unreturned phone calls. Louise encounters a flurry when we form a Cultural Diversity Committee and ask different departments to come and explain how they respond to diversity.

"Of course they're hostile," says Peter, "Because they're doing fuck all, pardon my language."

He's not quite right. There are initiatives and unconnected ideas that have been mooted. 'We need a policy paper – a Green Paper," says Usha who is chairing our new committee. "We don't need a budget. We need them to do something themselves."

I am having to learn, and it is a stretch. Paper, discussions, staff meetings, department meetings, more paper, more discussions, emails, memos. Where's the sense in it all? The outside world with all its real muddle and struggles and triumphs feels as if it's fading. What am I doing here? I look at agendas for staff discussion and see that yet again cultural diversity has not got on it. I pick up the phone again and again and again. And sometimes I want to put my head down on my smart blond desk and just weep. Does anyone know and understand what I am and what I deeply care about?

"I don't know why you take it all so seriously," says John as I thump the table back home. "After all, you're not black."

"That's not what it's about." I grit my teeth.

"And integration takes time. It's only been a generation. What do you expect?"

But when spring comes and the daffodils are out in Green Park where I take my sandwich lunch, I realise something. I discover that the Arts Council isn't a juggernaut as I'd thought. It's a set of villages. Some of them don't talk to each other. Some have individuals in them who are passionate and informed and very bright and who greet each other almost covertly with invisible freemasons' handshakes. Little quiet cabals, they keep members' spirits up and mine too and the flame alive. But god, it needs patience. Can we manage to turn this chunky machine around? Or part of it, at least?

Out in the country each regional arts board does employ an officer to cover cultural diversity. Why am I not surprised that mostly they are black or Asian and female and low down on the salary scale? Or that every one of them feels isolated, powerless and sidelined. But when we get together, it's as if we share a common language. At last, people who know what I am talking about! We are CDOG, and the new acronym slides silently into ACE-speak like a fish in water. "Change comes about though institutions," Usha said. But I still don't know how to bring it about. All we know is that the grassroots outside are a mile away from the bureaucracies where we work. Years ago, when we ran MAAS, I remember poor sad Feroze resigning from the Music Panel because he was expected to be the lone voice for all forms of ethnic diversity. How different are things now? We barely need to ask the question – but what is the answer?

There are times when I begin to feel bolder. It helps at times not to understand hierarchy. In my in-tray I find a tantalising circular from the British Council. How about a conference around the diversity theories developed by a certain Professor Homi Bhabha, it suggests? They are dense theories, couched in a furry overcoat of cultural studies-speak, but they still there's something that makes me sit up. "Listen, Louise – he's arguing that the debate around 'minoritarian' and 'majoritarian' culture has run its course."

"What sort of culture?" she asks.

"Awful words, but never mind that." I go on. "The whole debate has become, he says, – 'arid'. Arid is just how it feels to me, and has felt for a long time. "Instead we should be looking at the potential of the space between cultures."

I read on. I know our chief executive will like this too. I was on her board when she ran a small arts centre. So I scrawl a brief note on top

– "Exciting, don't you think?" – and send it through the internal mail. Back comes her reply. "Very!" Great!

I carry it in to my boss' office feeling like a trapper who's just bagged a bear. But my boss is not pleased. He is actually really angry. Officers should not, I learn, speak directly to chief executives. I can tell he doesn't believe I didn't know. He reads the circular again, turns it over, puts it down, picks it up again, looks out of the window. "Set up a meeting with the British Council people," he says. "Get some dates from my PA."

'Re-Inventing Britain,' declare the posters and the flyers and the banners outside the Brunel Gallery. Inside the seats are filling up at a great speed – arts officers, academics, local authorities, black and Asian arts practitioners, quantities of students. "It's not the usual mix," Usha observes over the rising growl and hum of conversation as we stand with Homi looking out surreptitiously from the wings: "That's good." She's right. These are people who usually live in their own enclaves. Academics don't speak to practitioners. Administrators don't talk to theorists. Local authority officers don't talk to academics. (And officers don't speak to chief executives.) Here they are sitting side by side and doubtless wondering who all the others are. And we've subverted the hierarchy too: we've got both top brass and officers.

I begin to see what Usha means about change happening through institutions. I could never have done this on my own.

And my friend the dancer's description of policy work is right too. It is wonderful. Trying to define it isn't all that easy. "It's an intellectual exercise. It means pulling back from the everyday and looking for root causes," I say to Usha, who is looking through her agenda and simply nods. This is what I love – looking to make a difference by small subtle changes, building in space for change. It is imaginative and respectful and it is democratic.

Some weeks later, the draft for a new Lottery grant comes round– a routine matter. I start to go through the conditions, and then stop and I go back to the beginning. "Louise, just look at this…" I say. She takes the paper and starts to read – "So…?" raising her eyebrows questioningly. Sitting quietly way down among all the criteria sits one criterion. In addition successful applicants, it specifies, must be able to show that they have responded to the needs of disabled people. It's small and innocent and unremarkable, and I know straight away it is the work of the Disability Officer, a canny ex-street-fighter who's come in from the cold. "Brilliant. The angel is in the detail. Wait and see." And so it turns out. Almost overnight new Lottery-funded buildings emerge that are accessible to people with disabilities: new jobs open out. "One little clause and a giant step for mankind."

This is worth giving up the open prairie, even though it's a tug. It comes down to writing and thinking and talking and shaping a Green Paper for a new policy and then a White Paper and more conferences.

"Are you off again?" asks John.

"There's a conference in Copenhagen. They want me to speak.'"

"I thought you were there last week?'

"No, that was Helsinki. Or was it Oslo, I can't remember. But I'll be back in time to collect George at the end of term."

"What's the difference? You're never here."

"So you noticed?"

"Fucking EU. The sooner we get out of that shower of freeloaders... You know what they're pulling in, what their salary is?" I shake my head. "Just hanging on the public tit," he goes on regardless, "And... y'know what?'" he roars out his favourite Daily Mail slogan – I put my hands over my ears – "'*You're paying for it!!*'"

I don't know what to think when the invitation to UNESCO comes through – the first outing of the Brits now that Tony Blair is in and the UK has rejoined UNESCO. But even John, with his violent distrust of arty liberalism is pleased. "What a shame your dad isn't alive," he says. "Wouldn't he have loved it!"

"Can't you see it? He'd have phoned all his patients and everybody he knows. 'By the way, did I tell you, Naseem's been selected to be part of the British government's delegation to the big UNESCO conference?' He'd have usurped it as his personal triumph."

We both smile, remembering Abba's total shamelessness. Outrageous, indefatigable – despite everything.

But too late, late by over ten years for Abba and for Mother – felled by bronchitis from too many cigarettes – too. What style Abba went out with though, the driveway right down to the road filled with flowers, and the pavement crowded with his patients all waiting to give him a good send-off.

And the smallness of him, I can't forget, when the undertakers arrived and so discreetly levered him into a body-bag that was like nothing but a large black hold-all. So small a man, such big aspirations – and how Stockholm would have satisfied him: hearing about that vast amphitheatre, our UK team sitting behind the official sign 'United Kingdom' just like in the movies. A confirmation of the success of his own journey from his birthplace in Bithli – a place so obscure it merits just one line in the tourist website, "No-one goes to Bithli".

"And don't forget Gerda," John goes on.

"Ah, Mother would have said, 'Ach, what a fuss...!'. She wouldn't have wanted to let me know she was impressed." But she would have been.

In the evening when the crowds have gone on to their official suppers, "You've got to see this," one of our Minister's civil servants whispers to me. I follow him along an empty corridor and into a little antechamber. A small designated group is already at work drafting the final communiqué; we show our passes and quietly slide into seats to watch. It's a change of gear. No more the vast formality of the enormous conference chamber or theatricals. It's all concentration. The Chair leads the representatives slowly and systematically through every word and every punctuation mark of the text. It is careful and undramatic. As he reads out each clause, one or other member of the team will say quietly, 'My government will not accept the word X' or "My government wishes to remove..." The word is taken out; the wish is accepted with no demur. "Page 13..." They work tirelessly with utter politeness, steadily, rhythmically. It could be boring but instead it's gripping. Time ticks by and I am unable to move. No shouting, no drama, no exiting as the Iranians did this morning in full assembly. Midnight comes, 1 a.m. Finally I force myself to get up and go back to our hotel. They are still there carrying on.

Walking slowly back through calm night-time streets, with a moon glinting on the harbour, I think this is how the world works. In backrooms with a selected few. It is like God writing on the stone tablets and saying "Here you are, Moses, Get on down the mountain with these."

When everyone reconvenes in the morning the draft is stacked neatly there, agreed, complete and printed up. We take it home.

It's full of high aspirations: Equality, respect, diversity. The nation has become 'cool' says our Prime Minister, and multiculturalism becomes part of the brand of Britain. I think I am becoming a paper hound. I write position papers, I present at conferences, I eat government papers for breakfast.

"Don't be fooled," says Peter when I drop round for a cup of coffee in the new flat he and his partner Diana inhabit, just behind Kilburn High Road. "They're a devious set of bastards."

"It's never going to work," he says roundly. "Just look at the evidence. Look at the budgets – the Music Department, all that money for what? For Western classical music, for orchestras and for the Royal Opera

House. Is the Music Department going to budge? Give up power? Not bloody likely."

We both remember the new broom who tried to cut one of the big orchestras and lost his job.

"Too much baggage. The only way we'd get anywhere is if they adopt zero funding."

"Meaning?"

"Meaning wipe the slate clean. Get rid of handicaps. Everyone starts at the same point."

I struggle with this. "I hate having to pick sides, them and us. It feels too simple. Maybe I'm getting soft?"

"Nah!" he laughs in a kindly way. "I'm just on my hobby horse. But still..."

"Do you remember going to visit Renee Short in the House of Commons way back, Peter?" It's one of my most humiliating memories.

He snorts. We both think of our arriving, after 'The Arts Britain Ignores' came out, both of us young and nervous, at the House of Commons with an appointment to see MP Renee Short. We'd been assured she would want to take on the cause of migrants.

"Did she, hell!"

She'd torn a strip off us – we couldn't expect any favours, she said. The working class had had to fight over time for equality and immigrants would just have to do the same.

"Oddly enough, in a way she was right. We have had to fight."

"But no-one will tell us to go away and be patient now."

"So there's been some progress?"

"Maybe." But it is not an upbeat 'maybe'.

I drive slowly home up West End Lane to our house at the edge of Hampstead Heath. No-one will be in. John's at a meeting at his club, George is in his second year at Sussex University. The house seems especially large and empty without John. He is not happy with silence. In the morning the radio has to be on in every room. The Today programme follows him from floor to floor to bathroom to kitchen. There's no getting away from news. "I might miss something," he argues.

It's evening but it's still light. A good time to sort out boxes of Abba's papers that my brother Anwar's passed on to me. It'll stop me thinking about Arts Council budgets and growing-up children.

I go and get them from the cellar and tip them out onto the carpet of our back room. Dear god, what a collection. Abba's kept everything. A handmade Eid card from his sister Fatima, wishing him 'A Happy

New Year' and also 'A Brilliant Success in the Exam' and also 'A Merry Christmas' – they clearly respect economising. The photograph of an elegant young man cut out and stuck carefully on the front looks like Jinnah. Certainly none of the males in my family, who tend to be homely and dumpy.

And here – why on earth did Abba keep all this – are sheets and sheets of unused letterheads for the India Relief Committee, 1943. He's kept all the responses – he must have been its Secretary – letters in strong forceful handwriting, from English well-wishers. They remind me of wealthy Mrs Cheney whom he visited when I was a child, and her high-minded benevolence "Dear Dr Khan, I willingly consent to the support the appeal as I have strong personal Interests in the welfare of India'. Abba, I see spells his surname with a self-invented circumflex over the 'a': Abba at his most swanky. At least he abandoned that bit of fakery. But bless him, here's a pencil sketch of where to put your feet in ballroom dancing – he was learning to do the foxtrot.

Deep down there's correspondence that tracks his even older attempts to establish himself. Can he extend his scholarship from the Fatema Bibi Charitable Trust? No, the reply comes back firmly. 'In addition to the scholarship amount, the trustees were good enough to allow you a sum of Rs800/- only for your outfit and travelling expenses which sum has already been paid to you before your departure from India". Maybe he can get a commission in the Indian Medical Service, he wonders in 1933. Unlikely, a grand-sounding English Lieutenant-Colonel replies – and "I am to say that candidates possessing better and higher qualifications have comparatively a greater chance of success."

I wince for my father.

The door opens with a rush of wind. It slams shut and the house – solid and Victorian though it is – shudders. John has arrived. He drops his coat and bag on the hall floor,

"You're home?" He goes into the adjoining kitchen and comes back with a large hunk of bread, mustard and honey-roast ham. "What are you doing?"

"Digging into history. Come and have a look. How was your trip?"

I go back to 1943, when they were raising money for the Bengal famine. The papers are wafer thin and the handwriting which is flowing and literate – way before the discovery of the biro – has faded. But the sentiments have not.

"They sent the draft petition to different English patrons, and Look at this, this man, a Mr J Hardy," – I pass his letter to John, "Careful, it's very fragile – writes back complimenting the draft but he says, "I don't like the sentence, 'Still the British people remain unmoved etc'. I should prefer to see it 'The British people will not remain unmoved etc'. So English!" But I see from the final version the British people remained unmoved...

"And the famine was caused by the Brits." There's a leaflet calling for people to demonstrate in 1942, to support the people of Contal who 'succeeded in overthrowing the British Administration and setting up a Government of the people'. Why have we never heard about this? 'But our alien rulers suppressed the Contal Government by force and by deliberate creation of famine'. 'Deliberate', you get it?" I wave the leaflet at John, "This man-made famine is now raging throughout Bengal!"

How shocking.

"Total crap."

"The famine's not crap. It's documented. Three million died!"

"And who's ever heard of Contal?"

"Not the point."

But he's lost interest and has picked up the Independent and is looking to see what's on television.

"Ah, this sounds good – Neolithic finds on Skara Brae."

The picture comes on slowly. A dry-looking man talks energetically to camera; behind him lines of people are creeping across a patch of bare ground examining it minutely. It looks very cold.

"Boring."

"It's heritage. You could learn something."

'Whose heritage?"

As I gather up all the flimsy bits of memorabilia that I'd had spread over the floor, I wonder about the heritage thing. Do you have it, like part of a passport? Or can it grow quietly without your noticing it? Can you catch a sense of heritage like a germ? I start to tell John, and then stop, about a sketch at Theatre Royal Stratford East – two young Asian street lads, comparing their trendy gear and clobber.

"So what's this one, bro?" asks one, fingering a large Om symbol round his pal's neck.

"Oh yeah, right, that's like, my Asian heritage, innit?"

'Right..' he agrees solemnly. 'Innit! They both cogitate, rocking on their heels.

"And this, man..?" He touches the even larger crucifix.

'That's for Jesus Christ, man. Jesus Christ who died for our sins, man," he recites glibly without taking a breath, "And after three days he rose again from the dead."

"Yeah, right on, bro." They nod in unison like those little dogs in the back windows of motor-cars.

It's a puzzle, this Englishness. I've acquired tag lines ("nothing but blood, sweat and tears...") and reference points. I'm tuned into English reticence and understatement and approve of them. I feel at ease when I come 'home' from abroad.

But somewhere in my background there are the tales of travelling forebears: the wolves of East Prussia, my great-grandmother who stipulated she should be buried in her bedsocks because she was always so cold. My father and other penniless Indian students sitting cross-legged on roundabouts to study in the light of streetlamps. The decaying haveli of my ancestors. The dignified tough simplicity of Islam. Heritage. My heritage.

Another week passes and every day I walk down Whitehall on my way to work, passing the edifices of empire, over-sized statues of military men whose achievements are proudly inscribed. I go past buildings that share the same quality of confident pomp – the War Office, the Foreign and Commonwealth Office. All of it declares history. But whose heritage? How can we sign up to this story when we have voices that call us from the other side?

"How do museums address this?" I ask Maurice Davis at the Museums Association, when we meet for a cup of coffee.

"It's a good question," he says. "Let's see if we can answer it."

So here we are, six months' later In mid November, Maurice and I and an Arts Council advance guard with the local CDOGs. The space is vast – it echoes; it is like several aircraft hangars rolled into one. Big arched ceiling and space for hundreds – well, thousands – of delegates. "Bloody hell, you'd need a rally to fill it," whispers one of the CDOGs awestruck. "We're not doing it here are we?"

We are about to embark on a two-day conference we've organised that will examine, dissect, interrogate and maybe reassemble the way the story of Britain is told. We have called it – of course – "Whose Heritage?"

Leaving the big shell, we troop with all our paraphernalia to the special conference centre adjoining the exhibition hall. Everything is in place. Tables, agendas, display panels, sound system. Any minute now the government's Secretary of State for Culture who'll give the first keynote speech is due. We fiddle around and make small talk, Louise, Arts Council bosses and me. It feels like waiting for a royal event. Then there's a sudden stir and a bustle and here he comes, surrounded by his entourage of young civil servants carrying his bags and his papers. The air ripples with that particular brand of urgency that brings UNESCO and Stockholm to mind. It immediately raises the temperature and says to everyone that something significant is about to take place. Power is entering the room. Arts Council top brass move forward smartly to guide the government team to the front and their reserved seats.

"What could they be thinking?" I mutter to Louise. The hall is still only half full. A little queue is building at the door where CDOGs are running down the lists of names at the desk by the door, but not nearly enough. But it does look as if most of the people queuing haven't registered. That could be a good sign. "Looking fine," said Louise reassuringly. It's true there's a good mix – at a glance, I can see activists and artists and archivists. And academics. I go and look over the shoulder of CDOG Pauline who is on the desk at her list. A lot of people who've said they are coming aren't here.

"Perhaps they've changed their minds?"

"Black people always come late. We always do. It's a bad habit. So don't worry," she whispers.

But down at the front I can see that our own director is fidgeting. We're nearly at the time we're supposed to start, but what can we do – the hall is gradually filling up. Too slowly for my liking. As more arrive, people are having to get extra chairs from the stacks at the back. No-one seems to want to sit down. They're greeting friends and gossiping. If this was a party it'd be a good one, But it's meant to be a conference.

The director is trying to catch my eye over the heads of delegates and he taps his watch meaningfully. What does he think I can do? In front of the top politician for culture in the country. It's going to be a huge massive failure. I can see it coming.

The director must have decided to take matters into his own hands because there's a stir at the front, and he's leading the Culture Secretary up the steps to the podium as if their presence in itself will impose instant order. But actually, it does. People hastily break off their conversations and settle down. We're off!

And he is so smart, Chris Smith. Louise and I look at each other and share a smile of admiration. He is so deft and so clear. A lot of the audience are sceptical about politicians, and white politicians, and white politicians speaking about black culture. But he is doing well. He puts his finger on it – "It's not a black and white thing," he says. "In order for society to know there is more than one interpretation of periods of history, we must be shown them." There's a rumble of assent, and I can see Maurice who's been wanting to have this fight for a long time, looking pleased.

There is appreciative applause when he's finished. He gathers up his papers and leaves the platform. Down below his entourage stand up and I wait for them all to take their leave. It is the politicians' way. They say their bit and they depart. But instead he sits down, and so does his team, as Stuart Hall takes his place. Good man, Chris Smith: he knows where the stars are.

So do many people in the hall. And if they don't, Stuart quickly shows them. He stands easily at the lectern, leaning on it, with one hand in his jacket pocket. He doesn't barnstorm. He doesn't harangue. He has a warm relaxed Jamaican mode of delivery. How quaint the term 'heritage' is, he muses. And how uncomfortable the English are with the term 'culture' . "They have to contain it safely, he muses, with the words 'Media' and 'Sport'. Smith – Minister for 'Culture, Media and Sport' – smiles. This is mischief: there's a ripple of kindly pleasure. We are safe.

I start to scribble notes on my conference agenda. 'Culture being constantly remade'. Don't look for uniformity or plain consensus – 'it is a place of dispute'. I underline 'dispute' because I can see this is going to be his theme. But I am wrong. It is not a standard declaration of oppression. Really? So where can he be leading us? He is slowing down now because, I think, he wants us not to miss a link in his reasoning. His rhythm is warm and considered, as if we're joining in a fireside chat. It feels as if it brings the audience together. We're just such a diverse lot, so argumentative and contentious and suspicious and bruised in so many ways. We are getting somehow lulled into unity. He is giving us, I realise, a picture not of polarity, but of flux. "The politics of recognition – as well as the politics of equality," I write. I underline "recognition". I am underlining almost everything now, my writing is going to be hard to decipher, crossings and re-crossings. "Not otherness". "Otherness" is a "negative figuration – reductive, simplistic"!

Chris Smith I can see is nodding vigorously, but I am too caught up to look to see how everyone else is taking it. But nevertheless, there is a feeling of concentration: a hush. Not 'other', stresses Stuart: 'different'. He pauses. And difference is part of the shifting panorama of global difference. We are mainstream: part of a great endeavour, the reshaping of culture.

"Questions?" asks the head of the regional Arts Council North West who is chairing the session. A hand goes up. He's talked a lot about blackness, asks a young white woman diffidently, but what does he think about whiteness and about white culture? He rolls his eyes as if he's been bowled a googly and everyone laughs sympathetically. "Answer...?" enquires the chair.

"Well, he finally says slowly, "I have nothing against whiteness. No. I just want you to know – it's... alright." He stops and continues judiciously. "Stronger on language than on the visual and so on. I think they're like everybody else. They've got their strengths and their weaknesses. I genuinely do." He pauses again. "I think negotiating with whiteness would be much easier if they saw themselves as a community among communities...

"Whiteness is only a problem when it is invisible, when it is the naturalised norm, when it is not a colour but The Colour against which all other colours are marked. When it is the background. Everything is really white but then occasionally a few people are black or brown.' He is enjoying himself playing with the idea.

"Whiteness as a kind of dominant and universal norm, that is the problem. Whiteness as specific and historical and changing and diverse and in trouble and not knowing exactly where it is – that whiteness we can talk to. They're just like us – confused!"

There are whoops and wows and applause as he finishes his extended riff. He looks around the audience with a kind of benevolent complicity. In my mind I can hear a rumble and a crash as the walls of separation fall down, like the walls of Jericho. They are there no more. No Racial Awareness Training as the RAT people would have it; no frustrated fury, no in and out, no them and us. Equal in flux. I think back to all the old closed compartments in my life – the secret meeting places of the Indian Association, the walls of the ghetto, even the foothills of international policy. It feels as if a tidal wave is bearing over all of them, with it come human stories, ability to shift and change. It is Wilson Harris's creative spirit and Homi Bhabha's subtle 'place in between.' It is Stuart.

He reaches the end – 'This is the bet, the wager," he says in conclusion, leaning forward, "This is the gamble that we are here to discuss". He puts his papers together, smiles and moves to the steps at the edge of the stage. Nothing happens for a few seconds. And then the audience rises too. Every single person, spontaneously: we rise to our feet and applaud. And applaud. And applaud. It goes on and on. No-one gives any sign of stopping. Stuart makes a gesture of deprecation but I am sure he knows exactly what he has done and the vision – for everyone – he has just delivered. Heritage? Our heritage. What we make it.

CHAPTER SEVENTEEN
2000

"The East End?" my brother's voice at the end of the phone sounds dubious. "Are you sure you know what you're doing? You know its reputation, don't you?"

"It's not Victorian times any longer, Anwar."

"Yes, but..." He isn't convinced, I know. He still thinks of visiting me in Ledbury Road and the Grove before it got fancy and people started calling it 'Notting Hill'.

"It's OK, we talked it all over. Amelia and George don't need a family home any longer now they've both finished university."

"And you're going to move to the East End?" He makes it sound like a heroin den. "What does John have to say to that?"

"He's got a flat in Soho." This makes Anwar pause. Soho has a seedy reputation too.

But he sounds wistful, "Do you have to do this, Naseem? Hampstead is such a lovely area." His voice drifts away and he sighs. There's really not much more to say. "Well..."

I realise that he is really concerned, and sad for me, my little brother. But yes, dear bro, I do have to do this. It is as if our marriage is a wall and now that our children are ready to move out, the mortar between the bricks has disintegrated. All the fault-lines John and I have been able to bury beneath work and family life for years have surfaced and are nipping at us daily. Twenty-five years haven't been enough to make them sink back and settle.

Demolishing the old house in Platt's Lane feels like unpicking decades of history. Actually, no *feels* about it. I am. Every room, every floor is stashed with objects of twenty years that we amassed to create the sort of family life that is no longer fit for purpose. Pictures, knick-knacks, furniture, memorabilia, pinboards, stocks of light-bulbs kept just in case, paint cans from paint jobs a decade or more ago, memorabilia, books.

Especially books. John's study is lined with bookshelves – a blessing bestowed by literary critic John Gross from whom we bought the house all those years ago. Floor to ceiling shelves on every side, where we merged our libraries. Reference books, Oxford syllabus novels, detective novels, school text books. John's Labour Relations books and scads of truly historic publications by the New Left Review that have an honest musty smell.

"Put them all in a skip," he says.

I could no more put books in a skip than I could eat my grandmother.

I call up book-dealer after dealer and they come and look. No, they say, they'll take what they want and leave the rest.

"All or nothing," I say determinedly. They smile pityingly and leave, one after the other. But I won't, I can't abandon the books, not even my scribbled on Sweets Anglo-Saxon Grammar or my school Latin texts.

I shout and rage at the objects "All this junk!" I yell at George.

"Calm down," he says soothingly. "Let's just take it one room at a time."

The cellar is full of it – John's old surfboard. Useless. Who'd surf on a wooden board nowadays? And it's splintered at the edges.

A broken cat basket

"No, it's not broken," George points out, "All it needs is a few straps. I can mend it. And you'll need it for the cat. Alien's coming with you." I am leafing through piles and piles of children's drawings, pulling out dead suitcases.

"And those might come in handy..."

A doll's house with the front missing. A metal trunk and inside it the children's old soft toys; George's old vast collection of Coca Cola cans from all over the world.

"Well, those can go out," he says cheerfully.

"You're joking! One day they'll be valuable. You'll be able to sell them and buy a house."

"Who's joking?"

But I do get tougher. Out go a wonderful array of old portable typewriters (including the one on which I'd typed the *Hustler* articles), stacked up outside the front door waiting for the bin man. Out go back-copies of innumerable magazines – back copies of Time Out – and newspapers, even children's paintings. Useless things.

My house in east London's Tower Hamlets won't accommodate them. Anyhow I want space, emptiness and a fresh start. I've had George Eliot's quote up on my wall for years: 'It is never too late to be the person you were meant to be'. And that's what I want.

But oh, the wrench of detaching oneself from the old...

Pictures come down and the walls behind are marked with pale rectangles where they'd been. Dealers arrive and smirk and point out faults in prints and antique bits of furniture. They really do say, "I'll do you a favour and take it off your hands..." I thought that was just a cliché in films. But I am too tired by now to argue.

Little by little our history disappears from Platts Lane.

Amelia calls from New York where she's just got a job,

"I'm going to come home for the weekend to help you pack up." When she arrives the three of us sit among the packing cases and eat takeway pizzas. There's a kind of high-pitched jollity, as if this is all a mad *fête champêtre*. I wouldn't mind this stage going on forever, me and my two kind, warm-hearted children. But Monday has to come, and Amelia flies back to her own life.

Occasionally John calls by, ringing the doorbell even though he still has a key. He's uneasy in this ending stage too.

"What shall I do to help?" he asks.

"How about collecting up all the spare paper that we haven't used to pack things?"

'Right." He disappears upstairs.

Half an hour later he returns clutching a sheet or two. "I didn't know what you meant."

I snatch them out of his hands.

The house is revealing quite a different character now. It's large and empty and our voices echo strangely in it. The pictures are gone. My father's old roll-top desk has gone to an auction house. Even the books have finally gone. When the last dealer also said he would take only a selection, I burst into tears and he hastily said, "Alright, alright! I'll take them all..."

But we are racing against the clock and when the last evening comes, neither George nor I go to bed. We pack and tape and pack and tape. But even if all had been packed and finished, I think we would still have wanted to sit up in respect for the house and the shelter it has given us.

I think back to Abba who provided some of the money for the deposit – only £37,500 for a six-bedroomed house near Hampstead Heath: impossible now, twenty years on. Twenty years ago, he'd phoned late at night.

"I'd just finished feeding you," I tell George." You were only a few weeks old." We'd chatted a little but I was tired, and so was Abba. Almost the last thing he said before we put the phone down was:

"Are you pleased with your property?" Safe at last, he must have thought, after all my long resistance to settling down.

"Very pleased," I said. And that evening, I tell George, he'd died. George is a master of knowing when to say nothing. He just puts an arm round me.

And the next day we move.

"It's always been an area that people have passed through, one way or another," the guide is declaring, or I think that's what she's saying. The noise of the traffic on the City Road booms and rumbles past, and I have to strain to hear. She's a dapper small woman who reminds me of a little pullet, dressed in an impeccable businesswoman's suit and clicking along briskly on the sort of high heels I wish I could wear. I crane over the heads of the small group massed around her. There's a red brick building in front of us – once, continues our guide, the Alexandra Dining Rooms. "It was run by the Laotian community," – "Who?" – but she's in full flow and won't stop – "who provided cheap hot meals for the poor." No sign of the mysterious Laotians now. Instead – almost next door – there's an entry to an underground bierkeller with an image outside of a vastly bosomed barmaid bearing twin steins of foaming beer. I guess they too have passed through.

"It's rather good value," says the woman next to me approvingly as we march on, following our guide over the City Road and into the depths of Shoreditch, down past Columbia Road ("the famous flower market"). "We really get to see a lot." It's true, though I'm a bit breathless. I glimpse what I still find it hard to call 'my house', but we are chivvied on – "Please don't dawdle". Taking an official tour seemed as good a way as any of finding landmarks in my new area. Goodness knows I feel I need them. I'd thought that moving house would be a simple affair. But it seems that I really haven't arrived – I am probably still a few miles away in my mind somewhere between Hampstead and now Shoreditch in the east.

I am losing my sense of direction. Our guide has a clear plan but we seem to be diving about here and there. Or maybe it's just that I haven't grasped my new neighbourhood fully yet, after all it's still just a few months and I have only the weekends off work when I can explore. George Dance built St Leonard's on the corner, and I gather that is impressive even though the name Leonard isn't and I have never heard of the saint. But I do know about Ben Jonson who hammered on the church door and claimed asylum when he killed Gabriel Spenser just over the road in Hoxton. "Shakespeare's first theatre was over there," she gestures in a westerly direction. "Neither theatres nor brewing were allowed inside the walls of the city of London. Several of his company are buried," she says, "in St Leonard's." How exciting. But where? The churchyard is all grassed over: not a sign of tombstones. "The graves are down in the closed-off vaults." More invisibles. And the theatricals have passed through too. We march on.

I have moved into a place that specialises in impermanence. Who stays? We peel off the layers as we circle around Shoreditch. We touch on furniture-making and all the small workshops dealing with areas of the craft. Hardly one now remains. We hear about Jewish and then Bengali sweatshops all down Brick Lane. Now they're gone too, replaced by the rancid smell of leather from scores of wholesale outfits, and spices from Indian restaurants crowded in a long Asian enclave. Each one sports notices announcing they've been awarded 'best' for this and that: It is like Alice – "All shall have prizes." We're back on Columbia Road now – home territory, just round my corner. A flower market since the 1920s, down Club Row there was a famous pet market "Till human rights people campaigned against it." I am not sure whether she considers this good or bad, or maybe just another example – pets and all – of even more passing through.

We skid to a halt on the corner of a large roundabout that's entirely taken up by a hill with a tiered garden. If we were to climb the steps, she says, we would see a disused bandstand on the top. We all generally shake our heads. The steps are dirty and don't look particularly safe. The bushes planted on the two tiers are dark and overgrown, with that glum dusty London look. Hard now to imagine it all in its days of glory, but there were days of glory, she says, and she ought to know. All around the bandstand is the Boundary Estate that was built in the 1890s for the deserving poor. "'Child of the Jago'" pipes up my neighbour knowledgeably and gets brownie points from our guide.

If I want heritage, I have it. It is here, but ghostly and half buried. Jewish Immigrants were here. Huguenots were here. Furniture makers were here. Shakespeare and his company were here. Passed through.

And now?

I live in a no man's land.

I sit in my Victorian corner house and try to puzzle its strangeness out. My street is odd for a start. It's tiny – just fifteen houses – and it exists on only one side. Where did the other side go? It's as if it got mislaid somewhere. Or was it taken out in the war? Instead of a line of mirror houses, we face a big estate car-park. Plumb in the middle there's a stubby 12-storyed Council tower block. To one side there's the handsome Victorian mansion block that I'd noticed in our march along Columbia

Road. On the other there's a long two storey 1960's block sitting over an underground car-park. And right at the far end there's a little alleyway that leads onto Hocker Street and the primary school. It all looks so random – could anyone have planned this hotchpotch of buildings and styles and heights? I think back to Platt's Lane just a few months ago, to its sleekness and sheer sense of entitlement. Does nobody here care?

There's a small group of Bengali women straggling their way over the big car park. I have a vantage point and watch them from my top window. Another woman is coming from the other direction, small, elderly and blue-rinsed. I know from the local shop that she's one of the original inhabitants of the estate. As she nears the women she imperceptibly slightly swerves. The Bengali women bunch together. No-one greets anyone.

"Jules Verne said that the person on the sidelines sees more of the game," I tell myself staunchly. But I would rather be a player.

We are mixed. We are Bengali and old East Enders who are still clinging on and a few incomers like me. "You moved from Hampstead here??" my neighbour who grew up here and brought her children up here says incredulously.

I thought I'd leave Platt's Lane and a new life would begin the next day. But even the cat, Alien, is having trouble with her sense of identity. Where are our anchors, and how long does it take to feel you belong somewhere?

Lists are good. They give the air of confidence. I make yet another – "Find a doctor, locate a hairdresser, repaint walls." There's a clatter as Alien struggles laboriously through the cat flap. She stops just inside the house and looks puzzled in a dazed sort of way. "Vet," I add.

When the days the Arts Council's allows for house moves are up, I walk to Liverpool Street to go back to work. The station is crowded, the signs are confusing. I am not sure which is north and which is south. I guess and find myself heading out east to Bow instead.

The ever-present concrete is a puzzle. The trees are few and far between, unlike Hampstead where they were proud old inhabitants. Trees in my area are anorexic and look as if they are gasping for breath. In the morning I find some of their thin branches have even been wrenched off in the night.

What happens in the night? In the daytime it feels quite sedate here. But at night-time it is as if a monstrous creature has got loose and is roaming the streets. The evidence is all around in the morning. Flagstones are levered up, the odd lamp-post pushed off true, bins overturned.

Pigeons are eating frigid takeaways strewn around the pavement. They fly with a metallic clatter as I pass. There is vomit.

I put out a hanging basket of petunias by the front door. It is stolen. I put out another and that goes too.

"I suppose I should be pleased someone likes it. I'd feel worse if it was just vandalised." I say to George, and I put out a third.

"Lovely," approves a passerby. But she doesn't see that I have padlocked it to the bracket.

It's three weeks in, and long past the allowed three grace days and Gascoigne Place still feels unliveable. Three weeks in and I still haven't been able to find my hairbrush in any of the unpacked boxes. I want to join Alien in sitting there looking miserable. She shies away when I try to pet her. She won't even let us see her eat. She waits till my back's turned and then she attacks her bowl of Felix. The sound of her urgent gobbling feels like an accusation.

Deciding about leaving the Arts Council is harder than I expected too. Once I've finally got settled, there's something comforting about the regularity of the Circle Line journey to Westminster, the ramshackle camp of protestors outside Parliament, the familiarity of the route to Great Peter Street and of the Arts Council. I even know the meaning of the acronyms now and can bandy them with the best. I've seen a quantity of Secretary-Generals come and go in seven years and undergone at least five restructurings. Hard to believe I found it all so burdensome at the beginning or that I thought everyone looked as if they'd been made by the same cookie cutter.

Time to go. Time to vacate my desk, turn in my pass.

I make my way for the last time to the tube, staggering under presents and copies of reports of all four conferences I devised. And who would have thought it – I feel sad.

Next morning I switch my alarm off and lie in bed watching the sun slowly making its way over the little tower block, Dunmore Point. In a few weeks I've got a day with a consultant to help me sort out a freelance life.

"You need to brand yourself," advises Amelia when she calls from her ad agency in New York.

"I am, I promise. I'm due to do an assessment of Women in Music, and an equality scheme for a Nottingham art gallery."

"Look at it as a new beginning."

Being based at home means I can see what I missed before. I never noticed the street life going on under my nose. It's not like Hampstead where people treated the street as a corridor. They'd speed into their houses and shut their front doors and only then start to live. People colonise these streets.

"Alright?' calls my neighbour, who has pulled her camping chair out onto the pavement to catch the last of the day's sun, as I walk past. Other family members slowly come out to join her. I step around them on my way to the corner shop.

"Alright."

I watch the daily traffic across the estate – the early morning passage of parents with little children in tow off to school; a small contingent of bright-legginged mothers bringing their middle-class kids to the nursery at the end of the road; the Bengali women who appear to meet every week in a barricaded small private club house at the end of the estate – more and more hijab-ed, I see, after 9/11.

"What do they do there?" I ask my neighbour who brought her children up here and knows everything. But she just shrugs in a huffy way.

"I wouldn't know. The Asians, they don't want to mix. They keep themselves to themselves."

Her daughter comes over to join us on the pavement with her baby girl.

"It's not right. Why should the Council let them use the building?"

"Well," says her mother significantly, "It's who you know, isn't it?" and taps the side of her nose.

Walking through the area is like walking through different bits of distinct territory. Asian, white, and creeping gentrification in other pockets. "How are you settling in?" asks Amelia when she calls from New York.

"The kids on the estate think I am 'posh'"

"I suppose you are."

"I don't feel it. But I do have a neighbour who climbed in when I locked myself out. You wouldn't get that in Hampstead..."

"The police would be round in an instant."

I hadn't noticed the sheer grubby beauty of the area when I used to do the daily Arts Council trek: home to tube, tube to home. Each of the buildings of the Boundary Estate that we'd skirted in our walking tour three years back is distinct. Somebody has thought about the estate. They didn't just run up identical blocks and pop people into each indiscriminately like plastic toys in a toy box. There are little curlicues here and there that make no practical sense, they just look appealing. And the rounded shapes of one building talk to similar shapes on the other side of the road. Where has all that thought gone?

One morning I happen to be crossing the estate when I pass two of the hijabbed women just as one accidentally lets her shopping bag go. It's windy in this bit of the car-park and papers start flying around. The two of them are rather ineffectually chasing bits and I bend down to help.

"I'm Naseem," I say as I pass over what I've gathered. "I live just over there."

"Naseem?" says the smaller one who has bright vole-like eyes above her scarf that she wears muffled round her mouth. Her cosier looking companion chases after the last bit of paper in a clumsy manner.

"Muslim name?" asks Vole-Eyes.

"Yes, my father..."

"Oh..." they look dubious. The old weariness hits – do I need to present a passport?

There is a brief exchange in Bengali and then with an indistinct mutter they scuttle away and I watch them retreat into the barricaded small building. Maybe my neighbours are right – "'They' don't want to mix..."

I wonder what Stuart Hall would have to say to all this. If we are all, as he claimed, equally confused, nobody here is owning up to it. We just seem to pointedly ignore each other.

Finally, I get the nerve to climb up the steps to the top of the little hill that is at the centre of Arnold Circus and the Boundary Estate. I can't see it's worth it after those years of anxiety. I'm in a wide empty tarmacked space, in the middle of it a broken-down bandstand. It must be aeons since it last heard music, and who anyway would want to come up here and listen to it? I'm high up – two tiers up – and should be able to see down the seven roads that spring out from the Circus like spokes of a wheel. But the bushes have all grown so tall and dark that it's impossible. They muffle the sound of traffic going round the Circus. I am almost entirely shielded up here from passers-by. Anything could happen to me. I leave.

"No, it could be really really beautiful," says Leila who is setting up a new café, on a corner next to the Circus. It strikes me this is super hopeful. There are some places that are clearly a lost cause.

"But the Bengali community won't go up there at all," she adds, "Ask Shehnaz." She nods to her young assistant.

"We're not allowed," she confirms briefly. "Bad people go there."

"Condoms, needles – all that," elaborates Leila cheerfully.

"But all it needs is for the bushes to be cut back and some new planting. We could do that ourselves, easily."

Nobody goes anywhere, it seems, when winter comes. None of the usual crowd of Asian youth that hang around aimlessly the corner of my street is to be seen. Even the little weekly group of women who cross to the mysterious little club room fail to appear.

"It's their fasting month, whatever it's called," says my neighbour. "You know, they don't eat."

Of course – Ramadan! The last time I experienced it was in Bombay the very instant the new moon was sighted and the whole night-time street exploded with joy. Horns honked, fire crackers erupted, strangers embraced: "Eid Mubarak!" I shall never forget it. Nor the time when I lived in Delhi, in Nizamuddin, – my quiet walks around the great tombs at the end of my little sandy street, breathing their dignified strength, the gravity of their architecture, the purity of the practice. How strange after all my skirting Islam to find myself plunged into the midst of a community for whom it is lifeblood.

Now that I know, I notice – when I happen to wake early – pinpoints of lights in the tower block coming on here and there in that half-light before dawn. I can tell which family is getting up to pray. It is like a network of morse code signalling across the estate: a silent community of faith. There are other signs too. My newsagent puts up notices, closes the shop and goes off to midday prayers in the mosque down the road. Anti-social behaviour, I am told, drops. Meanwhile in my own street, Christmas wreaths are starting to appear on front doors.

"It's self-segregation," says John when he phones. "Look at what happened in Oldham. And Blackburn." He is reading 'The Clash of Civilizations' and wants to convince me that multiculturalism is a vast mistake. "I don't mean your parents – your father wanted to be English. He respected Britain. But now all these women covering themselves up with those whatever-you-call-its."

"Hijabs."

"Burker things. They want to cut themselves off. They don't want to be part of Britain. I'd outlaw that for a start."

"You don't call Viriginia Water or... or Berkhampstead segregated. They're just as much ghettoes. But they're white."

"That's different, it's our country."

"But we're born here. It's ours too."

Why can't women wear hijabs if they want to? I really don't get it. But I give up.

"So when do you want to come over this way for a curry?"

It feels a modest form of co-existence, Ramadan prayers and Christmas wreaths.

"It's not like Oldham or Burnley. Nobody would riot here," I say to Leila when I drop by her deli-café for a coffee. She is absorbed, unwrapping packets of cheeses that will have – knowing Leila – been produced by small dedicated specialist dairies.

"No," she disagrees, "It's just as bad in its own way. Look at the narrow horizons the women have. I heard the other day about someone who was offered a job in Mile End, and she wouldn't take it because she'd never been out of the area. That's dreadful.

"And the school – you know it's almost all Bengali? – they always ask all the pupils in Year 5 what they see themselves doing when they leave school. And most of the boys last year said they wanted to work as waiters in Indian restaurants or drive a minicab. And the girls? No prizes for guessing... get married and have children." She sighs in exasperation and turns away. "It drives me mad!

"Oh by the way," she adds as she moves to the coffee machine, "If you feel like dropping by tomorrow evening, a few people are coming round. We're thought we'd talk about doing something about Arnold Circus."

"I think John is coming round – he wants to go down Brick Lane for a curry. I'll see if I can change it."

'Is he still living in Soho? Great place to be, all those wonderful little delicatessens."

"It's surprising – I never thought he'd manage on his own. He rings me up to find out how to cook things. It was fish yesterday."

He arrives wearing a pair of chestnut-coloured trousers that look very worn at the knee.

"That shows how little you know about England. It's really aristocratic to wear worn corduroys."

"Not that worn. They look as if you found them in a charity shop."

He looks dashed,

"Is it that obvious? But you must admit these shoes are pretty classy.'" He holds one foot out to show me his blue suede shoes.

No-one appears to notice his shoes, or his trousers, as we walk down Brick Lane. But then we are in the heart of trendy London and the narrow street is thronged with fashion statements massed around the clubs and vintage clothes outlet.

"That's what we used to call second-hand shops," I comment.

"Rubbish all this talk of austerity – there's endless money around, endless," he declares loudly as we push our way through the crowds.

On either side curry touts try to lure people in to their particular establishments. Special menu – free bottle of wine...

John bats them away and goes on talking. It's about halal food on school menus.

"When they come to this country..."

CHAPTER EIGHTEEN
2007

This is so nice. I could be in Sorrento, sitting here under the vine with green grapes plumping up and the early morning sun streaming into my back yard. Even Alien, who remained suspicious of Shoreditch long after I had softened, approves. I can see her stretched out where a pool of sunshine hits the bricks that pave my yard, in that lordly way that only cats can achieve.

I feel contented too. The picnic table is spread with books and papers and a laptop that links with an extension lead through the open kitchen window. A late butterfly – a Cabbage White – flits – by. What a good way to work, even though I have a puzzle in front of me. But an interesting puzzle. I've done surveys and evaluations and reports galore, but I've never done a Constitution.

It's got to be precise but not opaque. It's got to embody the spirit of what we are about but not be flowery. Difficult to avoid flowery because our project is all about transformation and how do you pin that down? It's about – we've all agreed – bringing Arnold Circus back to the people, jolting the sluggish heart of the Boundary Estate and getting it beating again. But try putting that down in legalese. The Charity Commissioners wouldn't give flowery-speak a second glance.

'Education', 'Public benefit', 'Heritage'. These are all good words. 'Poetry', 'beauty', 'transformation' are certainly not.

"Aren't we allowed to say it's beautiful?" asks Leila wistfully, in the last meeting when we went over it all.

"Well, maybe we can manage to squeeze it in somewhere..."

We've gone round and round in circles in Leila's after-hours cafe, enveloped in the homely smell of coffee and good cheese.

"Do we really have to have this?" asks Evon mutinously. "We were doing alright without it. We know what we're doing so why can't we just go ahead and do it?"

But there are a few mutters of dissent. Little by little a varied group has grown up over the year that we've met – architects, designers, a teacher, a museums administrator – who all want to see the old Circus come back to life

"All these hoops..." grumbles Evon undaunted.

"We've got to have a proper Constitution," says one of the architects firmly, "If we want the Council to take us seriously."

"The Council!" Leila takes a deep breath and casts her eyes up at the ceiling. "What have they ever done for the Circus? It's Listed, for heavens sake. They don't pay any attention to that!"

She's right. We even had a letter from them when we first began saying that Arnold Circus was "not a priority".

"If it was in Kensington, they'd never let it get in this state," says Jobeda hotly. "Just because we are a poor area..."

Well, I think, as I sit under the vine trying to craft a Constitution, being in an official Area of High Deprivation is good from the point of view of funding. I take another mouthful of coffee. It's gone cold. I look at my scraps of paper to work out what everyone said they'd wanted.

Number one – we want Arnold Circus (or Boundary Gardens as the Council will insist on calling it) to have beautiful planting. "Wild flowers," insists Leila. "And bulbs in season."

"Music, bands," added Evon. "That's what it was meant for."

And for me, it's got to reflect the diversity of people living on the Boundary estate round the Circus – around a third Bengali. "It can't be all white."

There are Aims and Objects in a Constitution. Maybe I can squeeze all this in somewhere. I call Anna, who is a museum administrator and who understands bureaucracy as well as I have had to.

"Send it over," she says crisply. "I can give it a look between eight and eight-thirty before I go to work."

"You know what I'd really like to see is a circus on the Circus."

She laughs.

"No, I'm not joking."

"Well, let's get a constitution and charitable status first."

"Just imagine, Anna, a trapeze artist among the trees and magic and clowns juggling. I bet none of the kids round here will have ever seen anything like that."

Mixing is so simple, I want to tell her even though I know Anna programmes herself tightly and I can sense she needs to get away,

"All these government papers about cohesion and integrating and parallel lives. People won't 'integrate' unless you give them a reason to do so."

I still have the advertisement stuck on my wall that Leicester paid to go in a paper in Uganda when Asians were being thrown out of the country in 1972. "Leicester's full up," it said, so, "In your own interests and those of your family you should not come to Leicester." But they did come, because they had friends and family there. Of course.

"There's no point in politicians wringing their hands and saying people 'ought to mix'. Why on earth should they if there is no reason, or inducement?" But then, I wonder, what is the inducement? A sort of magic glue...

I make a note to email my draft over to Anna before the morning and get up and stretch. George, who's moved into a shared flat in Harlesden, is coming round to collect his mail and probably use the washing machine. I put rice on to steam and chop up aubergines. It is so easy here, getting spices from the big Taj Stores down Brick Lane.

"When I was a kid," I declare to George over my shoulder, "We used to have to make a special trip all the way to London for my mother to get Indian spices, to a shop called Pataks."

"What makes you feel at home in a place?" I ask him over the sound of the onions sizzling.

"Well," he considers it slowly, "Are you sure you don't want any help?"

"I'm OK."

"Well, I guess it's like... when I've been away in another country," he muses, "And I get back and I can banter with the barman. That makes me feel at home."

"I think it's something to do with memories." I add. "Memories and the imagination. They tie a person to a place. And sharing memories, regardless of background, that's what creates community." The fat seems to sizzle in agreement.

This place is truly awash with shared memories. I go out of my way to talk to people in the street, in the Community Laundrette, on Arnold Circus itself, and people's versions of life in the old days on Arnold Circus and the Boundary Estate get richer and richer.

"Oh, the Boundary was a wonderful place, wonderful," says seventy-five-year-old Doris as we watch washing whirling around, and I can swear her eyes glisten. "All the women were friendly with one another. My mum used to do no end of washing to help the others and she washed the steps for the Jewish people. It was all Jewish then."

"We really should collect these memories," I say to Anna and Leila.

"All we'd need to do is to take a taxi!" Leila declares. "Every time I tell the driver where to go, he almost always says 'I grew up there...' and he tells me what it was like."

I hear stories of the time when the road was cobbled and when the horses came along "you could see the sparks from their hooves." And the times, says Ali, when he and other young Bengali lads used to hang out on the bandstand and smoke weed. "It's a good thing I got religion otherwise I could still be doing the same thing!"

I say to the group – now fully-fledged trustees of the charity Friends of Arnold Circus – "I bet there were feuds and that it wasn't all cups of sugar and solidarity." But still, people see it as precious.

When I get back home, I start to write in the diary I've kept since schooldays. It's quiet outside even though the big Hackney Road is so close. A few people pass in the street talking loudly and then are gone. There's the mosquito whine of a scooter – a pizza delivery for sure. I write about memory, how it forges such strong links to the present and provides a sense of identity.

'Shared memories,' I write the word and look at it. And then 'Integration?' And then 'Creating a shared past,' 'imagination.' Then I stop and think. How to get past all those gatekeeper-jargons – 'community cohesion,' 'participation,' 'ghettoisation' – that mean so very little? Can we transform Arnold Circus?

"A picnic," suggests Maki from the design group Abake who do all our charity's designs for love, in the next Friends meeting. "Bring people together. Invite them to come and picnic on the Circus and bring some extra food to put on a table for other people. We could call it a Sharing Picnic."

"Close off the road," Anna calls out over the noise of the 78 bus that uses the Circus as a turning circle at the end of its route, "So we don't have traffic hurtling round at least for one day." We cheer.

"Have a race to go a hundred times round the Circus," and the keen cyclists brighten. "But not competitive –anyone can join in, from kids with stabilisers to racing bikes."

"Get Spitalfields City Farm to bring a donkey and cart."

It's changing, the Circus is, beneath our very eyes. The dark vegetation has been cut back and reveals the broad expanse of the bandstand area behind it. Children from the primary school next door have climbed up the steps and been shown how to plant bulbs and throw down wild flower seeds.

"Two thousand bluebells," gloats Leila, "A thousand snowdrops and quantities of poppies..."

And at our first Sharing Picnic I can hardly believe my eyes. People have flocked up with rugs and picnics and children and little dogs. A long trestle table looks as if it bending under cakes, dips, samosas, bread. "All free, help yourself," beams Leila's assistant Shehnaz in a long white French-style apron.

It is as Doris said about the olden days, wonderful. Again. And it's not over yet.

Evon comes rushing over. "Guess who I've just been talking to. That guy who's going down the steps, you'll never guess what he does."

He doesn't look famous. He's large and unremarkable and has an ordinary comfortable air, what I can see of him.

"He's with a brass band and he loves the Circus and he wants to bring the band here!"

There is nothing, nothing like music to bring life to a place, even a place as rundown and shabby as our Circus. The strains of the theme tune from The Archers and 'Those Magnificent Men in their Flying Machines' and 'The Dam Busters' roll cheerfully down the radiating streets and the courtyards of the Boundary, somehow managing to be both celebratory and sedate at one and the same time. It is comfortable music. It encourages you to sit back and let the friendly oompah music of the Pavilion Brass Band in their smart purple coats roll warmly over us. It is like being licked by a nice dog.

The construction of bandstands, it turns out, is a magnificent natural amplifier. The sound flows easily down Calvert Avenue and around the Boundary Estate and the Circus returns to being the core of the estate. The nineteen blocks, named after Thames beauty spots, make sense architecturally. So lovely, I think, as I wander round their courtyards and every time find something fresh. The architects in the 1880s were all young, Leila says, often only in their thirties, and full of vision. If I look more carefully around me when I walk around the Boundary I can see I am walking through a utopian dream. This was planned to be the perfect estate for the old residents, everything on tap: schools, bath house, workshops and flats. And in the midst of it, the Circus itself, created to provide recreation – a chance to meet, socialise, listen to the music and – say the first accounts – even 'to flirt'.

"Flirting – how delightful," I exclaim. "Do you think anyone does that nowadays? What do people think about the area?"

"You could do one of your surveys," suggests Leila.

"Let's find out what the children at the school think of it."

It's more fun than doing a Constitution. Class 5 and 6 work at their surveys, sucking their pencils thoughtfully. How old do you think it is, they are asked to circle the one they think is right. Their answers veer wildly – five years? A hundred years?

"And what's underneath, do you think?"

"Bones."

"Dinosaurs."

"Monsters."

Asian people round the Circus agree with their youngsters. "It was a plague pit," older ones insist. "We won't go up there. Definitely not."

"And there's a tunnel," say the youths who still hang around the bandstand. "It goes all the way to the church at the end of the road."

"There's ghosts."

"Well, if not ghosts, most definitely dead bodies."

They all nod.

"The rubble of the old days, the slums they pulled down to build the Boundary," Doris had firmly said some months' back. And later that year we get a chance to find out who's right. It is astounding how lucky we are turning out to be. Out of the blue an email comes to me as Chair of the Friends. It's the Museum of London. They are wondering where to do their next community-based dig. How would we feel about them digging into Arnold Circus?

A number of weeks later, the smallest digger in the world – like something out of a child's story book – is carefully manoeuvred up the steps. It slowly chomps into the tarmac surface and drills down into the earth underneath. Finding what?

The hole is around ten foot deep, with a ramp going down into it. It looks like nothing but damp muddy earth when we peer over the safety barriers.

There is no tunnel. No dead bodies. What they bring up, all smirched with earth, are the long-buried relics of the Old Nichol, the vast and famous Dickensian slum that existed here before the London County Council ceremonially pulled it down in favour of a bright new modern future. They hadn't thrown the old debris out. They really had used it to make the hill that forms the Circus. And inside, shards and remnants of the lives of the old residents have been lying there hidden for over a hundred years.

We contact the school, and they send a class up, one after another, with a short break in between each. The Museum people give each child a kneeling mat and trowel and a very small yellow hard hat and invite them into the hole. They're doubtful at first. "Ugh, worms" shudders a Year 5 girl. "Creepy crawlies!" But once a few have started digging, the fever takes them; they all busy themselves scrabbling in the earth. And lo and behold, every single class finds something. The air rings with triumph, "Miss! Miss! Look what I've found..." It is the greatest of treasure hunts. A small child's shoe. Who owned it? Bits of clay pipes. Very varied bits of crockery "That's very interesting – it must have been one of their best dishes," says the Museum woman. "Mine's special," boasts the child who found it. They are elated and amazed, and struck that this commonplace area that they've known all their lives contains such history! No-one cares that they have not found monsters or dinosaurs. And then their mothers in their colourful hijabs and long concealing duster coats climb in and dig beside them. In between sessions, unseen, the Museum people adroitly bury the finds again and again so every single person is awed by the personal act of discovery.

It seems to me that they are writing themselves into history, and that direct connection – digging it up, handling it, smelling it – has to be what heritage is all about. Who was that child who lost her shoe? Why did they have best plates? Where did those people go after their belongings were thrown out?

Next day, one of the little Bengali girls from the dig runs past Leila's on her way to school. "Leila, Leila, Leila," she sings out. "I'm going to be an arkylologist when I grow up!"

As I walk back home that evening through the noxious passageway – ironically "Sweet Apple Place" on old maps – that leads to my house, I stumble across a couple of furtive young men hanging round its corner waiting for a drug-dealer. Further on, the recycling bins are overflowing with rubbish, and so is much of the estate itself.

It's horrible – even more now that Arnold Circus has refound its spirit. It's ugly. Right from the start of the estate where cars enter it, it's ugly. To the left there's a long patch that used once upon a time to be a flower-bed. Now it's high with weeds and full of dumped vodka bottles and beer cans and those mysterious silver phials that do goodness knows what.

"It's awful," my neighbour agrees, as she leans against the still warm front of her house. "Really awful. The Council should do something about it. Been like that for years."

"Can't we?"

"What?"

"Do something about it?"

"Why should we? We pay our Council tax, don't we?"

But back there, through the little passageway, there's Arnold Circus springing up now with poppies and ox-eye daisies, and people who come up to admire it and breathe it in. I can't stand the difference. I can't stand passing this mocking eyesore every morning that spits on the place where we live.

"It's the working class ethic," says John with authority drawn from his own working-class roots in Ilford.

"I don't care, and I don't believe it either."

I stand glowering at the wasteland one day when a stringy young woman with amazing topaz eyes gets off her bike. ""Something should be done about it," she says firmly. I turn in relief – a kindred spirit. "Yes! But what?"

"Flower beds, vegetable plots – doesn't matter. Just get rid of this fucking mess."

"I could do a questionnaire, find out what people want."

"Sounds good. I'm Katrina, by the way, – I live over there," she points to Dunmore Point. "And you won't believe the mess that's there too. This place is a disgrace."

"I could probably raise the money for a flower bed or whatever..."

"Really?"

"Well, I did for Arnold Circus."

There's a slight pause, and then she says a bit cautiously, "I suppose I could talk to a few people I know..."

It's not much, but it feels like a small inroad to the glumness of the estate. And then again, who knows – maybe nobody will want to get involved at all?

But crumpled notes start to float through my letterbox.

"Twelve people in all," I say to Katrina. "What a piece of luck. Otherwise we might have had turf wars."

A few of us are starting to pile compost into twelve beds, when a stranger walks along our little street. He stops when he catches sight of what we are doing, steps into the area, and without a word grabs a spade. He starts to heave earth vigorously into the beds and carries on like this for quite some time – none of us saying a word – until they are almost all half filled. "This is like being back in Ireland," he announces cheerfully. Then he puts his jacket back on, goes and we never see him again.

"Have you noticed," I say to Katrina, as the coriander and potatoes and Bengali hudu take hold, "how people are stopping to admire it, and ask people what they are growing?"

"Maybe there should be a bench there."

And when I peer out of my upstairs window, I can see the housebound

Bengali grannies have commandeered the bench and are sitting there keeping an eye on their grandchildren who are allowed to play out on the estate now.

One growing season passes, and another. The hudu get heavy and the coriander furls the growing beds with its light feathery green. Sarah's potatoes come up in straight lines

"That little house, at the bottom of the estate," my neighbour's daughter collars me one day indignantly. "It should be for everyone."

We all know that Bengali women meet in it every week. Beyond that it's locked and the windows are nailed shut with chipboard.

"It's not fair. It should be for everyone."

"We could find out."

"I tried years ago. I rang the Council but nobody would tell me anything." She shakes her blonde ponytail in irritation ands shifts her infant daughter onto her other hip.

She's right. I stop Vole-Eyes. So she is the shaker and mover who coaxed the Council into letting her women's group meet in the disused building. I should have known it. She's small but resolute and even inside the scarf she wraps round and round her head so it even covers her mouth I can catch a sort of upright steely quality that I like. She is her own woman.

"Maybe we could share it? We could paint it up, make it a bit nicer for you too."

"Mmm..." she says and looks into the middle distance.

"I don't know.You'd have to talk to the ladies," she says finally, but I can sense resistance.

"I'd like to – when should I come?"

Vole-Eyes eventually says, "Monday is better. I'll let the ladies know."

At last I shall see inside the hidden building! I am agog as I push open the door. Facing me are a few hijabbed women in the middle of a room filled with what looks like an awful lot of junk. They look apprehensive. Nobody says anything but I feel as if I am a fox that has invaded a hen-coop. What a dispiriting place to meet. The windows are covered by chipboard and the women have stuffed bits of old curtain and random cloth round them to make it even more secure. The room itself is piled up with varied unused bits of furniture like a lumber-yard and in one corner there's the largest photocopier I've ever seen.

"What's it for?" I ask Vole-Eyes, whose real name is Lutfa. She shakes her head.

"It's the Council's. They've never come for it."

And that's it. The place is really just one large room with a lobby and the grand number of three toilets attached. "That seems a bit excessive." She looks blank.

Seven or so women are seated stiffly round a formica table and they talk volubly to Lutfa when she explains what I've come to suggest.

"They don't think it would work," she says, which seems a short translation for an awful lot of Bengali.

"Why not?"

She looks a bit embarrassed. "Well... they say white people don't like them."

It's clear the women know more English than they are letting on because they are nodding decisively at this point.

"But how can they say that?"

"It's the looking. They look at us in a funny way," one of the women bursts out.

"How we dress," says another.

"They don't like how we dress. We can tell." There is nodding all around the table.

"We try to talk but they don't want to talk to us."

"Our English is not good," puts in a sharp-faced handsome woman, "We try to speak but we get as far as 'How are you?' and then we can't go any further."

"We are shy," says another.

"We are not against mixing," Lutfa insists.

"No, no," several agree.

"Then what should we do? I don't want to push you..."

"We would need a formal agreement with the Council – like a legal agreement" Lutfa says. "You'll need to talk to the Council."

"Is that what you did?"

"That's right."

"And then let's see how it works out."

They lock the door behind me as I leave.

"How's it going? Any progress?" asks Katrina after a few more weeks.

"Trying to find the right person in the Council is a pain. Sometimes I think they make it deliberately difficult." My respect for Lutfa is rising by the minute. She has managed to weave her way through the vast bureaucracy of Tower Hamlets. "The woman deserves a medal."

But when I finally get to the right person – which in itself takes many weeks – I discover Lutfa has been there before me, and without warning me has laid down terms.

"Your neighbourhood association can have a lease. But Mrs Miah has been in and she insists the ladies need a separate lease for the two days a week they've using the place," says the officer. I am shocked. Is this 'mixing'? Is this integration?

I go back to base. The more I think about it, the worse it becomes as a solution. Solomon said the baby should be cut in half, but it didn't make sense.

I seethe and then I subside. "Come round. We need to talk," I say.

She sits on the edge of my sofa looking wary and does not take her coat off. I feel nervous. Maybe this is a big mistake? "Listen," I finally say. "Do you know what white people say about Asian women? They say you don't want to mix with them." She looks up from her cup of tea. "If we give you a separate lease, then everybody will say, "There, you see, It's true, they don't want to mix.""

She looks down, harried but adamant – 'The women are very certain...' – and leaves her cup of tea half touched when she goes.

"We might have to forget it," I tell Katrina and she agrees.

And then days later, Lutfa's email arrives – You are right, it says: We don't want to give that impression. We have talked and we have decided we will join with you and we also want to be on your committee.

I cannot believe this, I want to hug Vole-Eyes and all the modest timid women who gather around her skirts. What honesty, what courage.

The lease is agreed: we have a rent of £1 a day and the responsibility for doing the place up. We have an integrated committee. Now to make the place – we call it The Hut – habitable.

Over one weekend a small army comes in dribs and drabs– not the general united turnout I envisaged, but here and there people turn up and take up a paint brush for half an hour or so and then head off. It's all a bit random and I can see Katrina with her painter's eye wincing. But we dash away, throwing out rubbish – an ancient microwave, dead kettles, an unexpected haul of children's games. The bins get fuller and fuller. And then I notice something odd and not too good just as Steve – who is a heavy-set local guy says it – "We're doing it up for them and bugger it, where are they?"

The people painting are all white.

My heart sinks. I can see everyone else making that same observation that has never till this minute surfaced. I don't want to catch anyone's eye in case it encourages them to pick up what Steve has just said. It seems rather than uniting, I have actually underlined difference. It is a dreadful moment.

And then, right then, I look out of the window whose frame we are carefully attacking with dark green paint. And over the carpark I and everyone else can see a small contingent approaching. It is half a dozen Bengali women. I recognise Mahmuda and Taslima and Roshida. And of course Lutfa. They are carrying containers and platters wrapped up in teacloths.

They have cooked and baked for us. The smell of samosas, bajiyas and pakoras – all hot and fresh – reaches us before they do. Everyone lays down their paintbrushes.

"We hope they are alright for you," says Lutfa as she gives out paper napkins. "We know you don't like our spices so we have made them not too hot."

"Can't be too hot for me," says Steve, and general noises of appreciation join him. The plates are being emptied at a breakneck rate and the women themselves are beaming.

"Try this," they go round urging, "And this... Very mild. Not too hot."

Afterwards a couple of them stay and gamely try to paint, but it's clear they have never done it before and before long they are off.

"Better that they stick to cooking," says Katrina sotto voce. "That's what they do really well." As they leave it is to a chorus of goodbyes and thanks.

At the end of the day, we stand back and look at the space, capacious and echoing – everything (except for the vast photocopier) has gone – and smelling new with fresh paint. There's something about space that makes people go quiet, or maybe it's just tiredness. We clean our brushes and stack up the empty paint cans and I do a sum. "Forty people," I say to Katrina, "Taking part over the length of the day."

"Not bad..."

I make my way over the car-park to my own house, passing the vegetable beds on my right. I can see others of our team making their own way home to different bits of our mismatched estate, and for a moment I feel almost affectionate towards its odd brutal quirkiness. But maybe that is what belonging means. Maybe it comes from the ground up, and it happens when the imagination is engaged. I think back over years to the rough and raw impact of the Fasimbas, to the warm rhetoric of Stuart Hall, to all those many many individuals putting their experiences of loss, love, joy, bewilderment, pain in the public arena, right down to the personal discoveries of the little kids the other day on Arnold Circus. There's a connection there.

How to work it out? Engaging the imagination leads to empathy; empathy leads to a sense of connection – a breadth of vision and sympathy; connection leads to a feeling of belonging. A three-step simple progression and it ends in breaking down barriers. At the heart of the process are the arts, but it spreads wider. For the imagination, as I remember Wilson Harris stressing all those years ago, is a subtle beast. It stretches our potential far beyond what we might have considered possible, crumbling all sorts of barriers and definitions that have set themselves up. So why do we value it so lightly? Build it so rarely into the basis for our civic life? It is the uniting factor: magic glue, linking public and private lives.

I am not sure if the development on this one London estate – or on Arnold Circus – has been a triumph or is simply a small and shaky step. But I can think back to scores of misunderstandings, of avoidance and misapprehensions over the years, when people turned their backs on each other to stop having to look each other in the face. To the overall ongoing struggle to make a place for ourselves on this little island. To the old bitter polarities. And when I now consider today's political scene with its miserable seeping xenophobia, this seems OK. Drill down into the moment and barriers collapse and an astonishing range emerges. Everywhere is somewhere – no confinement. Identity is not a place to end. I'll settle for this. For the moment.

BACKGROUND

This is not a documentary or an objective work of record even though it exists within the framework of events in the public arena.

I've attempted to recreate my own feelings and responses – as the child of double immigrants – to major social changes as I've lived through them. To help me I have gone back to cuttings, files and documentation and to diaries that I have kept since childhood. I have also used the web and drawn on books that bring back the spirit of the times – Sam Selvon's stories, for instance, and Colin McInnes' novels.

If you wish to get more facts and a sense about events, here are some – though by no means all – of the books I have used.

Arthur Mee's Children's Encyclopedia, vols 1–10

CHAPTER 4
'Black British, White British." Dilip Hiro Penguin 1971
'Ayahs, Lascars and Princes' Rosina Visram Pluto 1986

CHAPTER 6
"Rhythm in the Heavens' Ram Gopal, Secker 1957
'Maha-Maya' Nartaka,Bangalore, 2012

CHAPTER 7
'Thanks for Coming' Jim Haynes Faber 1984
'Hippie Hippie Shake' Richard Neville

CHAPTER 8
New Beacon Books
'Lonely Londoners' Sam Selvon
'From Michael de Freitas to Michael X' M Abdul Malik, Deutsch.
'Colour and Citizenship' EJ B Rose and Associates. OUP 1969

CHAPTER 9
'Bloody Foreigners' Robert Winder Little, Brown 2004
'The Politics of Community Action' Jan O'Malley. Bertrand Russell Peace
Foundation 1977
'There Ain't No Black in the Union Jack' Paul Gilroy
'The Caribbean Artists Movement 1966-1972' Anne Walmsley New
Beacon 1992
'Black Panther: the art of Emory Douglas' Rizzoli 2007

CHAPTER 10
'Area of Darkness', VS Naipaul
'My Son's Father' Dom Moraes
'Indian Muslims' Maulana Wahiduddin Khan Al-Risala Delhi 1994

CHAPTER 11
'All Together Now' Steve Gooch Methuen 1984
'The Turning World: stories from the London Festival of International
Theatre' Rose Fenton and Lucy Neal Gulbenkian 2005
'Let's Get It On' Catherine Ugwu ICA 1995
'Dreams and Deconstructions' ed Sandy Craig Amber Lane 1986

CHAPTER 12
'The Arts Britain Ignores' Naseem Khan Gulbenkian Fondation, Arts
Council CRC 1976
'Beaton but Unbowed' Norman Beaton Methuen 1986
'The Caribbean Artists Movement; Anne Walmsley New Beacon Books
1992

CHAPTER 13
'The Arts Britain Ignores' Naseem Khan CRC, 1976
"On Route: the art of Carnival' ed Pax Nindi Xpress 1988
'Behind the Masquerade' Kwesi Owusu and Jacob Ross Arts and Media
Group

'CHAPTER 15
'Our Creative Diversity' UNESCO 1995
'The Politics of Heritage' ed Jo Littler and Roshi Naidoo Routledge 2005
'The Location of Culture' Homi Bhabha

CHAPTER 16
'The Blackest Streets' Sarah Wise Bodley 2008
'Family and Kinship in East London' Michael Young and Peter Willmott Penguin 1957

CHAPTER 17
'The Art of Regeneration' Comedia 1996 (Nottingham conference papers)
'A Sense of Place, a Sense of Time' John Brinckerhoff Jackson Yale 1994.

Everywhere is Somewhere. The Final Draft

Epilogue

M um got diagnosed with cancer in January 2016.
By the time that they had found the cancer, it had spread from the lungs into the liver and into the bones. There was nothing that could be done. It was a Stage IV terminal diagnosis.

A terminal diagnosis is always devastating. For mum who was so healthy and so full of life it was almost impossible to comprehend. But she understood it more clearly than we did, approaching her illness with imagination and curiosity and treating it as way of learning more about life, even if she didn't have much more of it left.

She was very loath to tell anyone that she was ill. She was very clear that she did not want cancer to define her. And it never did. Life continued.

Even at the very end when the cancer had moved into her spine and she could not walk, and then into her throat and she could not eat and drink, mum was still remarkably active and positive. "It never broke my spirit, you do know that", she told us in the days before her death.

She worked on the final edit of this book from hospital.

She found out that it would be published on Tuesday 6th June.

On Wednesday 7th she took a sudden turn for the worse. We had to sign the contract on her behalf as she couldn't talk or focus.

She died peacefully in the early hours of Thursday 8th June.

This book that was so important to her would have an audience.

Amelia and George